Measurement and Calculation

for the Trades

Sue Grecki

Workplace Educator

Bob Whitaker

Certified Carpenter, CA, CQ

SkillPlan BC Construction Industry Skills Improvement Council

Library and Archives Canada Cataloguing in Publication

Grecki, Sue, 1956-

Measurement and Calculation for the Trades / Sue Grecki

ISBN 0-9685027-9-2

1. Numeracy. 2. Workplace literacy. I. SkillPlan (Program)
II. Title.

QA141.G74 2005   513   C2005-906020-4

Second Printing
Copyright 2008
SkillPlan BC Construction Industry Skills Improvement Council
Lynda Fownes, Executive Director
All rights reserved.

To order copies of this publication, please contact:

SkillPlan – BC Construction Industry Skills Improvement Council
Suite 405, 3701 Hastings Street
Burnaby BC V5C 2H6

Order online: www.skillplan.ca

Design and Layout:
Greater Than Graphics, New Westminster, British Columbia

Acknowledgements

Measurement and Calculation for the Trades is the result of SkillPlan's experience tutoring hundreds of trades workers and sharing teaching strategies with our union network of trades instructors. We sincerely thank all of these individuals.

The impetus that initiated this project is a now out-of-print text developed and published in 1981 by Joel Kositsky, Bobbi Flint and Bill Darnell. These dedicated trades workers knew their craft, the required math skills and practical approaches to learning them. Fondly known as the "green math text", this text became a standard not only in the carpentry trade but for apprentices and journey workers in other building trades. Our thanks is extended to the BC Provincial Council of Carpenters and Construction Labour Relations Association, a joint labour and management training committee, who have generously allowed us to build on this legacy.

Workplace Educator, Sue Grecki has designed this publication using the framework of its predecessor. She has updated the instructional portions, subtracted some of the elementary math fundamentals and added more challenging sections. For the past ten years Sue has had the privilege of working with apprentices, journey workers, trades instructors, content experts and training coordinators to learn about how they use measurement and calculation on the job.

Bob Whitaker in his roles as provincial Trades Coordinator for BC and instructor has guided countless young men and women through the years of apprenticeship required for journey worker status. His contribution to this text is his in-depth knowledge of the trade. He provided many of the drawings and commented on the practice problems. This team approach blends the best of education with the best of construction craft.

SkillPlan acknowledges the financial contribution of the National Literacy Secretariat, Human Resources and Skills Development Canada for the development of materials that support a skilled workforce.

About *SkillPlan*

SkillPlan, the BC Construction Industry Skills Improvement Council, was formed in response to the learning needs of an evolving industry. The construction workforce requires increasingly higher levels of reading, writing, numeracy, problem solving and oral communications skills. *SkillPlan's* mandate is to provide a solid foundation of these Essential Skills, the Velcro ™ to which all other training sticks. Essential Skills are part of an adult's life at work and in his or her union and community.

Numeracy skills are an integral part of success both on the job and in technical training. Heat and Frost Insulators and Sheet Metal Workers use geometry, trigonometry and triangulation to draw patterns of both regular and irregular shapes. Boilermakers, Glaziers and other trades workers measure and cut materials using metric and Imperial measurements. Carpenters, Plumbers and Operating Engineers use decimals of a foot and decimals of an inch to measure and calculate. Cement Masons calculate the volume of concrete required in cubic yards or cubic metres. The list is endless.

Measurement and Calculation for the Trades is another addition to the growing library of resources that support workplace essential skills. You might be interested in the related publications, the Numeracy Rules kit and Tools for the Trade: A Guide to Success in Apprenticeship.

SkillPlan is a joint labour and management initiative of the construction industry in British Columbia. It was established as a not-for-profit society in March 1991. For more information, visit *SkillPlan's* website at *www.skillplan.ca*.

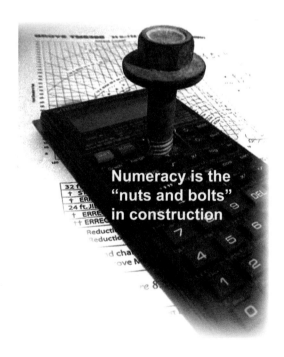

Numeracy is the "nuts and bolts" in construction

Table of Contents

Preface

Whatever trade you choose, you will need Essential Skills like reading and math. Because trades focus on physical know-how, skills like reading, document use, measuring and calculating are often hidden. As a trades worker you will study prints, get information from product labels, check safety regulations, and refer to many codes and regulations. Your math skills will also be put to the test in every trade. No matter what aspect of building you decide on for your career, you will measure and calculate – every day.

Sometimes apprentices find technical training challenging. They love the work, but find returning to a classroom tough. Measurement and Calculation for the Trades can be used in both informal and formal settings by individuals or groups. Preparing for technical training by practising and reviewing the required numeracy skills makes it easier to relearn skills and retain new learning. It is SkillPlan's hope that this resource contributes to success in technical training and on the job.

Over the years, SkillPlan has worked with hundreds of apprentices and journey workers. With this experience, SkillPlan has produced this text to help you learn math foundations. Learning the basics will allow you to use these math skills for measuring and calculating applications in the building trade you choose as a career.

The first five chapters review basic math skills in whole numbers, decimals, fractions, ratio/proportion and percent. The chapter on measurement and conversion reviews the Imperial measuring system and the International System of Units (SI), also known as the metric system. Both measuring systems are used by apprentices and trades workers in the construction industry. Apprentices and journey workers often know one of the measuring systems but are unfamiliar with the other. Working with fractions while using Imperial measurements is challenging for many trades workers. Regardless of the units, the saying "measure twice and cut once" is never truer than on a construction site. Errors in time and materials are costly. These chapters are a good place to start if your math skills need a thorough review.

The second half of the math book begins with an introduction to using formulas. The four chapters in this section are Perimeter, Area, Volume and Right-Angle Triangles. You will likely find these chapters more complex.

The chapters can be completed in sequence or by topic. The answer key is at the back of the book. As you build your confidence in mastering these foundational skills, you will need to challenge yourself with some trade-related problems. This is a good way to test your understanding of measurement and calculation. Order the accompanying publication for your trade applications at *www.skillplan.ca*.

INTRODUCTION

Trades workers in the construction industry perform basic math skills on the job every day. Adding, subtracting, multiplying and dividing whole numbers are used in measuring, averaging, estimating and blueprint reading. As a trade worker you need to be able to add, subtract, multiply and divide both in your head and using a calculator.

Being able to do basic calculations with whole numbers quickly and easily makes it easier to work with fractions, decimals and other math skills. When you have completed this section you will be able to:

❐ Add, subtract, multiply and divide whole numbers.

❐ Use the order of operations to calculate an equation that has more than one operation.

❐ Use addition, subtraction, multiplication and division to calculate a missing dimension.

PLACE VALUE

Understanding Place Value

The number system we use is called the decimal number system because its base is ten. Each digit in a written number has a "place value". You know what its value is by its place or location in the written number.

The value of each place is 10 times as large as the value of the place to its immediate right. The value of each place is 10 times as small as the value of the place to its immediate left.

The number 21,673 can be placed in the diagram like this

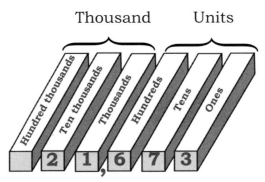

and read "twenty one thousand, six hundred seventy-three".

Write the place value of each underlined number.

1.   4<u>3</u>11<u>6</u>   3 _____   6 _____

2.   9<u>00</u> <u>3</u>56   0 _____   3 _____

3.   <u>7</u>9<u>6</u>5   7 _____   6 _____

4.   <u>2</u>11,3<u>5</u>5   2 _____   5 _____

Also Look!

For more on zeros and place value look in the section on Decimals.

Zeros and Place Value

Zeros are placeholders. When you are adding, subtracting, dividing and multiplying whole numbers, you need to remember to use zeros as placeholders or you will get the wrong answer.

350 $\Longrightarrow$ The zero holds the ones or units place.

3,500 $\Longrightarrow$ The zeros hold the ones and tens places.

7,050 $\Longrightarrow$ The zeros hold the hundreds and ones places.

Reading and Writing Large Numbers

Step 1: Start at the right side of the number. 546789<u>1</u>

Step 2: Separate the numbers into groups of three.
5 467 891 or 5,467,891

Step 3: Read each group of three numbers followed by the value of that group.
5 million, 467 thousand, 891

Did you know?

Groups of numbers can be separated using spaces or commas: 200,312 or 200 312

Rounding Whole Numbers

To round a whole number, follow these steps:

Step 1: Underline the number in the place you are rounding to.

Step 2: If the digit to the right of the underlined digit is greater than or equal to five, round up. Add 1 to the underlined digit. Change all the digits to the right of the underlined number to zeros.

5<u>3</u>9 $\Longrightarrow$ 540

Step 3: If the number to the right of the underlined digit is less than 5, leave the number as it is. Change all the digits to the right of the underlined number to zeros.

2,<u>3</u>28 $\Longrightarrow$ 2,300

Estimation means finding a reasonable answer. An estimate is not exact, but it is close. Rounding the numbers in a problem is a good way to estimate an answer. Estimating on the job is an important skill. Errors mean a loss of time and money.

Round each number to the nearest 10.

1) 13   2) 164   3) 289   4) 2 843

Round each number to the nearest 100.

5) 139   6) 551   7) 8 344   8) 10 648

Round each number to the nearest 1000.

9) 1 296   10) 3 514   11) 28 399   12) 51 903

ADDITION

CARRYING

Remember:

- $0 +$ any number = that same number
  $0 + 42 = 42$
- $1 +$ any number = the next number
  $1 + 13 = 14$
- The order you add numbers in doesn't matter.
  $4 + 8 = 12$
  $8 + 4 = 12$

Carrying:

You can write a small number:
- at the top of the next column
- carry the number mentally to the next column

Example 1:

Ones
Tens

```
  2 8
+ 4 7
```

Step 1: Start on the right.
Add $8 + 7 = 15$.

```
  ¹
  2 8
+ 4 7
    5
```

Step 2: Write down the 5 and carry the 1.

```
  ¹
  2 8
+ 4 7
  7 5
```

Step 3: Add the tens colum.
Remember to add the carried 1.

Carrying More Than Once

Sometimes you must continue "carrying" as you add the columns from right to left.

Example 2:

$$\overset{1}{2}89$$
$$+\ 436$$
$$\overline{5}$$

Step 1: 9 + 6 = 15.
Write down the 5.
Carry the 1.

$$\overset{1\ 1}{2}89$$
$$+\ 436$$
$$\overline{25}$$

Step 2: Add the "carried" 1 + 8 + 3 = 12.
Write down the 2.
Carry the 1.

$$\overset{1\ 1}{2}89$$
$$+\ 436$$
$$\overline{725}$$

Step 3: Add the "carried" 1 + 2 + 4 = 7.
Write down the 7.

Add the following.

1) 89
   +17

2) 136
   +48

3) 47
   +94

4) 82
   +19

5) 902
   +18

6) 456
   +544

7) 28
   +82

8) 77
   +54

9) 8
    5
   +4

10) 9
     9
    +3

11) 13
     72
    +89

12) 91
     13
    +17

SUBTRACTION

Subtraction is the opposite of addition. You can check your answer in subtraction using addition.

Example 1:					
	12	–	3	=	9
	9	+	3	=	12

Example 2:

$$37 \qquad 13$$
$$\underline{-24} \qquad \underline{+24}$$
$$13 \qquad 37$$

BORROWING

Borrowing:

You can write a small number:
- at the top of the next column
- carry the number mentally to the next column

Example 1:

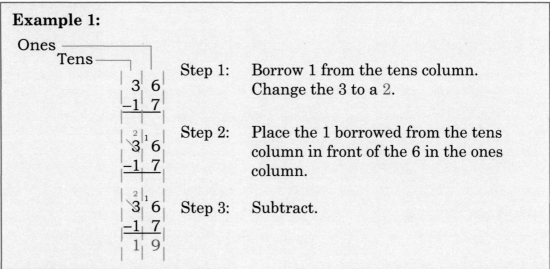

Step 1: Borrow 1 from the tens column. Change the 3 to a 2.

Step 2: Place the 1 borrowed from the tens column in front of the 6 in the ones column.

Step 3: Subtract.

Hint:

Most errors are caused from not lining up the numbers correctly: ones, tens, hundreds and so on.

Borrowing More Than Once

Example 2:

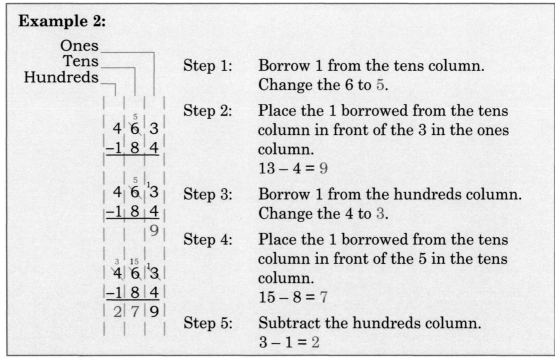

Step 1: Borrow 1 from the tens column. Change the 6 to 5.

Step 2: Place the 1 borrowed from the tens column in front of the 3 in the ones column.
$13 - 4 = 9$

Step 3: Borrow 1 from the hundreds column. Change the 4 to 3.

Step 4: Place the 1 borrowed from the tens column in front of the 5 in the tens column.
$15 - 8 = 7$

Step 5: Subtract the hundreds column.
$3 - 1 = 2$

Borrowing With Zeros

You cannot borrow from zero. When you are borrowing and you come to a zero, you move to the next column to the left.

Example 3:

$\overset{1}{\cancel{2}}04$
$-\ 89$

Step 1: You cannot subtract 9 from 4.
You cannot borrow 1 from the zero in the tens column.
Borrow 1 from the hundreds column.
Change the 2 to a 1.
Place the 1 borrowed from the hundreds colum in front of the 0 in the tens column.

$\overset{1\ 9}{\cancel{2}\cancel{0}}4$
$-\ 89$

Step 2: Borrow 1 from the tens column.
Change the 10 to 9.
Place the 1 from the tens colum in front of the 4.

$\overset{1\ 9}{\cancel{2}\cancel{0}}\overset{1}{4}$
$-\ 89$
$\overline{115}$

Step 3: Subtract the ones.
Subtract the tens.
Subtract the hundreds.

Subtract the following numbers.

1) 50
    - 6

2) 60
    - 8

3) 98
    - 9

4) 34
    -17

5) 117
   - 28

6) 313
   -168

7) 574
   -486

8) 924
   -446

9) 201
   -99

10) 506
    -87

11) 100
    -31

12) 400
    -42

MULTIPLICATION

Multiplication is a fast way to add repeated numbers. Following the rules of multiplication, you can perform multiple addition in one operation.

Example:

A carpenter worked for 23 hours at $24 an hour.
How much pay did he earn in all?

To solve this problem you could add:
$24 + $24 + $24 + $24 + $24...... 23 times.

You can perform this multiple addition in one operation by multiplying $24 × 23.

$$\begin{array}{r} \$24 \\ \times\ 23 \\ \hline \$552 \end{array}$$

THE MULTIPLICATION TABLE

Having these facts in your head will allow you to carry out many math calculations more quickly.

More complex math calculations will be easier because you know your multiplication tables.

Reading the Multiplication Table

You need to know basic multiplication facts quickly and accurately. Take the time now to memorize them.

Example:

$7 \times 9 = 63$

	1	2	3	4	5	6	7	8	9	10	11	12
1	1	2	3	4	5	6	7	8	9	10	11	12
2	2	4	6	8	10	12	14	16	18	20	22	24
3	3	6	9	12	15	18	21	24	27	30	33	36
4	4	8	12	16	20	24	28	32	36	40	44	48
5	5	10	15	20	25	30	35	40	45	50	55	60
6	6	12	18	24	30	36	42	48	54	60	66	72
7	7	14	21	28	35	42	49	56	63	70	77	84
8	8	16	24	32	40	48	56	64	72	80	88	96
9	9	18	27	36	45	54	63	72	81	90	99	108
10	10	20	30	40	50	60	70	80	90	100	110	120
11	11	22	33	44	55	66	77	88	99	110	121	132
12	12	24	36	48	60	72	84	96	108	120	132	144

CARRYING IN MULTIPLICATION

Example 1:

$$\overset{1}{2}6 \\ \underline{\times\ 3} \\ 8$$

Step 1: Multiply 3 × 6 = 18.
Write down the 8, carry the 1.

$$\overset{1}{2}6 \\ \underline{\times\ 3} \\ 78$$

Step 2: Multiply 3 × 2 = 6.
Add the carried 1.
Write down the 7.

Example 2:

$$2\overset{2}{7}6 \\ \underline{\times\ \ 4} \\ 4$$

Step 1: Multiply 4 × 6 = 24
Write down the 4.
Carry the 2.

$$\overset{3}{2}\overset{2}{7}6 \\ \underline{\times\ \ 4} \\ 04$$

Step 2: Multiply 4 × 7 = 28
Add the carried 2.
28 + 2 = 30
Write down the 0.
Carry the 3.

$$\overset{3}{2}\overset{2}{7}6 \\ \underline{\times\ \ 4} \\ 1104$$

Step 3: Multiply 4 × 2 = 8
Add the carried 3.
8 + 3 = 11
Write down the 11.

Example 3:

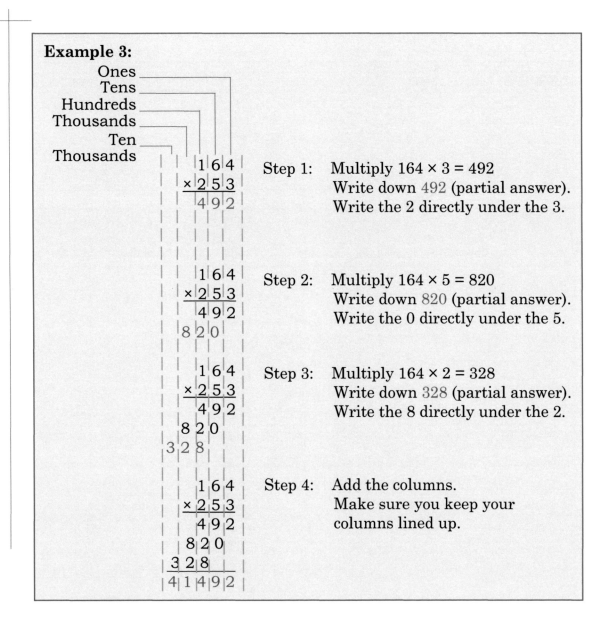

Ones
Tens
Hundreds
Thousands
Ten
Thousands

164
×253
492

Step 1: Multiply 164 × 3 = 492
Write down 492 (partial answer).
Write the 2 directly under the 3.

164
×253
492
820

Step 2: Multiply 164 × 5 = 820
Write down 820 (partial answer).
Write the 0 directly under the 5.

164
×253
492
820
328

Step 3: Multiply 164 × 2 = 328
Write down 328 (partial answer).
Write the 8 directly under the 2.

164
×253
492
820
328
41492

Step 4: Add the columns.
Make sure you keep your
columns lined up.

Multiply the following.

1) 42
  × 21

2) 13
  × 13

3) 71
  × 71

4) 912
  × 37

5) 782
  × 104

6) 612
  × 108

7) 521
  × 805

8) 711
  × 100

DIVISION

Division is the opposite of multiplication. Division separates a given quantity into equal parts. For example, how many two feet pieces can be made from a 12 foot 2 × 4?

Division can be shown several ways:

$$257 \div 9 = \qquad\qquad \frac{257}{9} \qquad\qquad 9\overline{)257}$$

LONG DIVISION

Keep your numbers lined up and do one step at a time.

Example 1:

$6\overline{)342}$

Step 1: 6 does not divide into 3.

$\begin{array}{r} 5 \\ 6\overline{)342} \\ 30 \\ \hline 42 \end{array}$

Step 2: Divide 6 into 34.
34 ÷ 6 = 5
Write 5 in the answer space.
6 × 5 = 30
Write 30 under 34.
34 − 30 = 4
Write 4. Bring down the 2.

$\begin{array}{r} 57 \\ 6\overline{)342} \\ 30 \\ \hline 42 \\ 42 \\ \hline 0 \end{array}$

Step 3: Divide 6 into 42.
42 ÷ 6 = 7
Write 7 beside the 5.
6 × 7 = 42
Write 42 under 42.
42 − 42 = 0

Step 4: Check your answer.
57 × 6 = 342

Example 2:

Sometimes there are zeros. Remember:
Zeros hold places.

$$7\overline{)3507}$$

Step 1:   7 does not divide into 3.

$$\begin{array}{r} 5 \\ 7\overline{)3507} \\ \underline{35} \\ 0 \end{array}$$

Step 2:   Divide 7 into 35.
$35 \div 7 = 5$
Write 5 in the answer space.
$7 \times 5 = 35$
Write 35 under 35.
$35 - 35 = 0$

$$\begin{array}{r} 50 \\ 7\overline{)3507} \\ \underline{35} \\ 00 \end{array}$$

Step 3:   Bring down the 0.
7 does not divide into 0.
Write 0 in the answer space beside the 5.

$$\begin{array}{r} 50 \\ 7\overline{)3507} \\ \underline{35} \\ 00 \end{array}$$

Step 4:   Bring down the 7.
Divide 7 into 7.
$7 \div 7 = 1$
Write 1 in the answer space beside the 0.
$7 \times 1 = 7$
$7 - 7 = 0$

$$\begin{array}{r} 501 \\ 7\overline{)3507} \\ \underline{35} \\ 007 \\ \underline{7} \\ 0 \end{array}$$

Step 5:   Check your answer.
$501 \times 7 = 3507$

REMAINDERS

Answers do not always come out evenly when you are dividing. When there is an amount left over, it is called the remainder.

Example:

$$\begin{array}{r} 121 \\ 8)\overline{971} \\ \underline{8} \\ 17 \\ \underline{16} \\ 11 \\ \underline{8} \\ R3 \end{array}$$

Step 1: Write the answer as 121 R3

Step 2: Check your answer the same way as for other long division.

121 × 8 = 968

Add the remainder.

968 + 3 = 971

Divide the following.

1) $2)\overline{248}$ 2) $8)\overline{168}$ 3) $5)\overline{215}$ 4) $7)\overline{224}$

5) $12)\overline{264}$ 6) $28)\overline{868}$ 7) $31)\overline{868}$ 8) $57)\overline{1\,824}$

9) $5)\overline{5\,025}$ 10) $4)\overline{436}$ 11) $30)\overline{6\,030}$ 12) $21)\overline{2\,205}$

13) $16)\overline{283}$ 14) $21)\overline{487}$ 15) $26)\overline{973}$ 16) $39)\overline{1\,637}$

ORDER OF OPERATIONS

When an equation combines more than one operation, you must follow the order of operations. An operation is a mathematical process such as addition, subtraction, multiplication or division.

Example:
$(15 + 6) \div 3 + 4 \times 2 - 3^2$

The acronym **BEDMAS** is an easy way to remember the order of operations. BEDMAS tells you the order to do calculations.

Hint:

The exponent tells you how many times to multiply the base.

base $\rightarrow 3^2 \leftarrow$ exponent

$3^2 = 3 \times 3 = 9$

$3^3 = 3 \times 3 \times 3 = 27$

	Symbol	Example
Brackets	( )	$(15 + 6) \div 3 + 4 \times 2 - 3^2$
Exponents	3^2	$21 \div 3 + 4 \times 2 - 3^2$
Division	$\div$	$21 \div 3 + 4 \times 2 - 9$
Multiplication	$\times$	$7 + 4 \times 2 - 9$
Addition	+	$7 + 8 - 9$
Subtraction	-	$15 - 9 = 6$

Example 1:

$$5 + 8 \times 7 =$$

There are no brackets, exponents or division so the first calculation is multiplication. The last calculation is addition.

$$5 + 8 \times 7 =$$
$$5 + 56 = 61$$

Example 2:

$$8 \times 16 \div 4 =$$

There are no brackets or exponents so the first calculation is division. The last calculation is multiplication.

$$8 \times 16 \div 4 =$$
$$8 \times 4 = 32$$

Calculate the following.

1) $9 + 8 \times 3 =$

2) $6 \times 8 + 6 =$

3) $13 \times 2 - 2 =$

4) $20 \times 10 \div 5 =$

5) $36 \div (8 - 2) =$

6) $(20 - 11) \div (6 \div 2) =$

7) $20 \div (2 \times 5) =$

8) $(35 \div 7) - (8 \div 4) =$

9) $5^2 - 6 \div 2 =$

10) $9 \times 5 + (7 - 2) - 4^2 =$

PRACTICE

1) The following deliveries of 2" × 6" were made to a job site:

> 1 728 board feet
> 1 634 board feet
> 892 board feet

How many board feet of 2" × 6" were delivered?

4254 board feet.

2) An apprentice works 152 hours in January, 138 hours in February, 149 hours in March and 155 hours in April. How many hours did he work during those 4 months?

The apprentice worked 594 hours

3) The cost of materials for a job were as follows:

Lumber ---------- $2 812	Hardware ------ $97
Concrete-------- $254	Gravel---------- $48
Pipe ------------- $115	Other ----------- $26

How much did the materials cost?

$3352.⁰⁰

4) A contractor used the following figures to estimate the amount of hardwood flooring needed.

Bedroom #1--- 144 sq. feet	Living Room -- 206 sq. feet
Bedroom #2 -- 168 sq. feet	Dining Room - 184 sq. feet
Bedroom #3 -- 128 sq. feet	Kitchen -------- 133 sq. feet

What total should he use to calculate his estimate?

963 sq. feet

5) $83 was deducted from a worker's wages of $596. How much money did the worker take home?

6) A roof is 1 174 square feet. Fifteen sheets of plywood have been used to cover 480 square feet. How much area is there left to cover?

694 is left to cover.

$$\begin{array}{r} \cancel{1}\cancel{1}74 \\ -480 \\ \hline 694 \end{array}$$

7) A wall was 251 mm shorter than the footing at each end. The footing was 3 447 mm. How long was the wall?

the wall is 3698mm long.

3447-25/×2.
3447- 502
2945

$$\begin{array}{r} 3447 \\ +251 \\ \hline 3698 \end{array}$$

8) A shed costs $5 718 to build. How much does it cost to build 17 of them?

$$\begin{array}{r} 5\ 15 \\ 5718 \\ \times\ 17 \\ \hline 40026 \\ 5118 \\ \hline 97206 \end{array}$$

9) Cove moulding is bought in 8 foot sections. How many feet are there in 37 pieces?

10) One sheet of plywood is 1 220 mm wide. What width would 13 sheets cover?

11) Seventeen board feet of hardwood are required to make a coffee table. How much wood is required for 14 tables?

12) Twelve snap ties are used in each sheet of plywood on an outside concrete form. How many snap ties are needed if 97 sheets of plywood are used?

13) A carpenter uses 518 nails to install 7 sheets of floor plywood. How many nails does he use in each sheet?

$$\begin{array}{r} 74 \\ 7\overline{)518} \\ 49 \\ \hline 28 \\ 28 \\ \hline 0 \end{array}$$

14) An apprentice cuts 3' pieces out of a 16' long 2 × 4.

   a) How many pieces can he cut out of one 2 × 4?

   b) How long would the left over piece be?

15) A trades worker cuts 9" pieces from an 96" piece of plywood.

   a) How many pieces can he cut?

   b) What is the length of the remaining piece?

16) A trades worker uses 7 nails to assemble a door header. A box of nails contains exactly 1 000 nails.

   a) How many headers could he assemble using 1 box of nails?

   b) How many nails would he have left over?

17) A house is built on 16 footings. Each footing requires 7 cubic feet of concrete and 23 feet of reinforcing bars.

   a) How many cubic feet of concrete are required in total?

   b) How many feet of reinforcing bars are required in total?

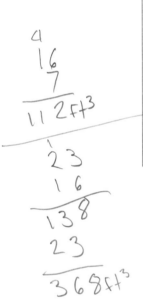

18) An apprentice can nail a sheet of plywood in 6 minutes. How long will it take to nail 24 sheets?

19) How many lineal feet of cove moulding is required for a dining room that measures 12' × 16'?

20) On three consecutive days, a crew of four labourers worked eight hours. Calculate the total number of hours worked by the crew.

INTRODUCTION

Decimals and fractions are both ways to name all of the possible numbers that are less than one or are between whole numbers. Using decimals allows you to complete calculations using your calculator.

When you have completed this section you will be able to:

- ❐ Add, subtract, multiply and divide decimals.
- ❐ Convert fractions to decimals and decimals to fractions.
- ❐ Calculate decimals of a foot.
- ❐ Calculate decimals of an inch.
- ❐ Solve word problems using decimals.
- ❐ Solve applications using decimals.

PLACE VALUE

Understanding Place Value

All decimals have a value of less than one or less than a whole. You can compare a decimal fraction to a fraction whose denominator (bottom) is always a number like 10, 100, 1 000, 10 000 and so on.

Example :

$0.6 = 6$ tenths $= \frac{6}{10}$

$0.05 = 5$ hundredths $= \frac{5}{100}$

$0.32 = 32$ hundredths $= \frac{32}{100}$

$0.004 = 4$ thousandths $= \frac{4}{1000}$

$0.267 = 267$ thousandths $= \frac{267}{1000}$

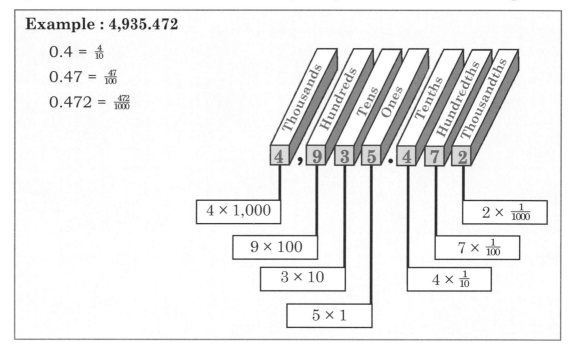

In decimal notation, only the numerator is actually written. You can figure out what the denominator is by the position of the decimal point.

Example : 4,935.472

$0.4 = \frac{4}{10}$

$0.47 = \frac{47}{100}$

$0.472 = \frac{472}{1000}$

Zeros in Decimal Numbers

Zeros hold place value, just like whole numbers.

> **Example :**
> $0.3 = \frac{3}{10}$
> $0.03 = \frac{3}{100}$
> $0.003 = \frac{3}{1000}$

You can add one or more zeros to the right side of the decimal number without changing the value of the number.

$0.3 = 0.30 = 0.300 = 0.3000 = \frac{3}{10}$

Rounding Decimal Numbers

You round decimal numbers the same way you round whole numbers. There is only one difference. After you round to a given decimal place, you drop all the numbers to the right of that number.

Step 1:   Underline the number with the place value you are rounding off to.

Step 2:   Look at the number to the right.
- 5 or more, round up
- less than 5, stay the same

Step 3:   Drop all of the numbers to the right of the number you rounded off to.

> **Example 1:**
> Round 5.27 to the nearest tenth.
>
> 5.2̲7   Step 1: Underline the number with the place value you are rounding off to.
>
> 5.2̲⑦   Step 2: Look at the number to the right.
>
>   7 is greater than 5 so round up.
>
> 5.3   Step 3: Drop all of the numbers to the right of the number you are rounding off to.

Example 2:

Round 15.604 to the nearest hundredth.

5.6_04   Step 1: Underline the number with the place value you are rounding off to.

15.60④   Step 2: Look at the number to the right. 4 is less than 5 so stay the same.

15.60   Step 3: Drop all of the numbers to the right of the number you rounded off to.

Round off to the nearest tenth.

1) 5.43   2) 2.37   3) 15.398   4) 238.001

5) 17.938   6) 1.882   7) 456.709   8) 322.1622

Round off to the nearest hundredth.

1) 91.444   2) 26.375   3) 2.056   4) 1.005

5) 12.0384   6) 18.032   7) 5.0382   8) 0.01252

Round off to the nearest thousandth.

1) 1.0344   2) 10.5116   3) 19.9994   4) 32.76553

5) 155.3333   6) 43.8827   7) 26.7469   8) 717.2296

READING DECIMALS

Step 1:   Read the number. $0.56 \Longrightarrow$ fifty-six

Step 2:   Say the place value of the right-most number.
$0.5\underline{6} \Longrightarrow$ fifty-six hundredths

$\Downarrow$

hundredths

MIXED DECIMALS

Step 1:   Read the whole number first. $10.35 \Longrightarrow$ ten

Step 2:   Read the decimal. 10 point

Step 3:   Read the decimal part. 10 point thirty-five

Step 4:   Say the place value of the right-most number.
Ten point thirty-five hundredths

Hint:

It's okay to say 'and' instead of point.

Hint:

Sometimes a decimal fraction will be written as 0.8. You do not need to say the zero. It is still 8/10.

CONVERTING A FRACTION TO A DECIMAL

Step 1:   Divide the numerator (top) by the denominator (bottom).

Examples:

$\frac{1}{4} = 1 \div 4 = 0.25$

$\frac{1}{2} = 1 \div 2 = 0.5$

$\frac{3}{4} = 3 \div 4 = 0.75$

Hint:

Check out the chapter on fractions for more information.

Convert the following fractions to decimals. Round off to the nearest thousandth.

1) $\frac{5}{8}$ 2) $\frac{1}{4}$ 3) $\frac{11}{16}$ 4) $\frac{3}{8}$

5) $\frac{1}{3}$ 6) $\frac{24}{56}$ 7) $\frac{33}{66}$ 8) $\frac{127}{227}$

CONVERTING A DECIMAL TO A FRACTION

Step 1: Drop the decimal and draw a line under the number. This number is the numerator.

Step 2: Count the number of digits and write this many zeros. Write a 1 in front of the zeros. This number is the denominator.

Step 3: Express fractions in the lowest terms.

Example 1:
Convert 0.25 to a fraction.

$\underline{25}$ Drop the decimal and draw a line under the number. This number is the numerator.

$\frac{25}{100}$ Count the number of digits and write this many zeros. Write a 1 in front of the zeros. This is the denominator.

$\frac{1}{4}$ Express fractions in the lowest terms.

Example 2:
Convert 6.75 to a fraction.

$6.\underline{75}$ Drop the decimal and draw a line under the number. This number is the numerator.

$6\frac{75}{100}$ Count the number of digits and write this many zeros. Write a 1 in front of the zeros. This is the denominator.

$6\frac{3}{4}$ Express fractions in the lowest terms.

Hint:

See the chapter on fractions for how to express fractions in lowest terms.

Remember:

A mixed number has a whole number and a fraction.

Convert the following decimals to fractions.

1) 0.3   2) 0.7   3) 0.04   4) 0.39

5) 0.90   6) 0.004   7) 0.084   8) 0.091

9) 0.137   10) 0.871   11) 0.442   12) 0.0001

13) 6.4   14) 3.14   15) 7.02   16) 40.01

17) 0.15   18) 9.08   19) 31.812   20) 1.004

21) 328.76   22) 408.2   23) 6.222   24) 81.05

ADDING DECIMALS

Step 1:   Write the numbers in a column with the decimal points lined up.

Step 2:   Add zeros as needed to the right of the decimal point.

Step 3:   Add the same way you add whole numbers.

Step 4:   Place the decimal point in your answer. Write it under the decimal point in the column you added.

Example:
Add 2.085, 11.32 and 0.214

2.085	Line up decimals.
11.320	Add zeros as needed.
+ 0.214	Add the same way you add whole numbers.
13.619	Place the decimal point.

Add the following decimals.

1) 25.811   2) 62.4   3)   1.2147   4)   3.1076
     4.29   20   12.54   16.4
      3   9.82   1.88   3.2091

5)	7.2 m	6)	22.4 ft	7)	7.3628	8)	17.260
	0.841 m		4.22 ft		1.014		451.0001
	0.02 m		0.667 ft		79.53		1.989
	1.9 m		5 ft		2.1006		92.7433

SUBTRACTING DECIMALS

Step 1: Write the numbers in a column with the decimal points lined up.

Step 2: Add zeros to the right of the decimal point.

Step 3: Subtract the same way you subtract whole numbers.

Step 4: Place the decimal point in your answer.
Put it under the decimal point in the column you subtracted.

Example:

A carpenter shortens a 2.815 m board by 1.267 m.
How long is the remaining piece?

$$
\begin{array}{r}
2.815 \\
-\ 1.267 \\
\hline
1.548
\end{array}
$$
The remaining piece is 1.548 m.

Subtract the following decimals.

| 1) | 3.89 | 2) | 8.8 | 3) | 31.85 | 4) | 30.88 |
| | − 1.45 | | − 7.6 | | − 20.63 | | − 29.9 |

| 5) | 3.768 | 6) | 3.5 | 7) | 5.7 | 8) | 700. |
| | − 1.549 | | − 1.76 | | − 4.667 | | − 0.001 |

MULTIPLYING DECIMALS

Step 1: Multiply the numbers as if there was no decimal.

Step 2: Count the total number of decimal places multiplied together.

Step 3: Start at the right of your answer and count the total number of decimal places. Count the same number of spaces and move the decimal place to the left. Place the decimal point.

Remember:

Put in more zeros if you need them.

Example 1:

```
  1.3   1 decimal place
× _4    0 decimal place
  5.2   1 decimal place
```

Example 2:

```
  1.25    2 decimal places
× _1.2    1 decimal place
  250
 1250
 1.500    3 decimal places
```

Example 3:

```
    3.1416    4 decimal places
×    _9.72    2 decimal places
    62832
  2199120
 28274400
 30.536352    6 decimal places
```

Multiply the following decimals.

1)
```
   1.2
×  _9
```

2)
```
      2
×  0.4
```

3)
```
   1.8
×  _4
```

4)
```
   2.1
×  1.3
```

5)
```
   2.75
×  1.03
```

6)
```
   2.18
×  0.85
```

7)
```
   1.002
×   0.03
```

8)
```
    48.2
×  0.001
```

DIVIDING DECIMALS BY WHOLE NUMBERS

Step 1: Set up the problem like you do for whole number division.

Step 2: Place the decimal point directly above the decimal point of the number you are dividing into.

Step 3: Divide the same way you divide whole numbers.

Step 4: Check your answer using multiplication.

Example 1:

$75.6 \div 7 =$

$7\overline{)75.6}$ Set up the problem like you do for whole number division.

$7\overline{)75.6}^{\,.}$ Place the decimal point directly above the decimal point of the number you are dividing into.

$7\overline{)75.6}^{\,10.8}$ Divide the same way you divide whole numbers.

$10.8 \times 7 = 75.6$ Check your answer using multiplication.

Example 2:

$12.9 \div 4 =$

$4\overline{)12.9}$ Set up the problem like you do for whole number division.

$4\overline{)12.9}^{\,.}$ Place the decimal point directly above the decimal point of the number you are dividing into.

$4\overline{)12.3}^{\,3.225}$ Divide the same way you divide whole numbers.

$3.225 \times 4 = 12.9$ Check your answer using multiplication.

Dividing Decimal Numbers by Decimal Numbers

Step 1: Set up the problem like you do for whole number division.

Step 2: Move the decimal point in the divisor enough places to make it a whole number.

Step 3: Move the decimal point in the dividend the same number of places. Place the decimal point above.

Step 4: Divide the same way you divide whole numbers.

Step 5: Check your answer using multiplication.

Example 1:

$118.02 \div 2.1 =$

$2.1\overline{)118.02}$ — Set up the problem like you do for whole number division.

$2\underset{\curvearrowleft}{1.}\overline{)118.02}$ — Move the decimal point in the divisor enough places to make it a whole number.

$2 1.\overline{)1180.2}$ — Move the decimal point in the dividend the same number of places. Place the decimal point above.

$\begin{array}{r} 56.2 \\ 2 1.\overline{)1180.2} \end{array}$ — Divide the same way you divide whole numbers.

$56.2 \times 2.1 = 118.02$ Check your answer using multiplication.

Divide the following decimals.
Round off your answers to the nearest thousandth.

1) $2\overline{)56.8}$ 2) $11\overline{)35.97}$ 3) $14\overline{).042}$ 4) $4\overline{)254.8}$

5) $6\overline{)3.462}$ 6) $3\overline{)9.822}$ 7) $2\overline{).525}$ 8) $10\overline{)1.874}$

9) $0.4\overline{)2.8}$ 10) $1.3\overline{)5.2}$ 11) $0.02\overline{).42}$ 12) $1.2\overline{).96}$

13) $115\overline{)13.8}$ 14) $0.08\overline{)2.040}$ 15) $0.33\overline{)9.999}$ 16) $1.15\overline{)27.55}$

17) $0.001\overline{)42}$ 18) $0.03\overline{)2.1}$ 19) $0.03\overline{)21.0}$ 20) $2.15\overline{)38.7}$

DECIMALS OF A FOOT

In North America, structures are usually laid out in feet, inches and fractions of an inch. Unfortunately, fractions are more difficult to use when estimating quantities and calculating differences in elevations. Because it is easier to perform calculations using whole numbers and decimals, it is important to know how to convert inches and fractions of an inch to decimals of a foot.

Decimals of a Foot Conversion Table

The table below, Decimals of a Foot Conversion Table, gives you all of the conversions from $\frac{1}{8}$" to 12" rounded off to two decimal places.

INCHES

F		0	1	2	3	4	5	6	7	8	9	10	11
R	**0**	.00	.08	.17	.25	.33	.42	.50	.58	.67	.75	.83	.92
A	$\frac{1}{8}$	.01	.09	.18	.26	.34	.43	.51	.59	.68	.76	.84	.93
C	$\frac{1}{4}$	.02	.10	.19	.27	.35	.44	.52	.60	.69	.77	.85	.94
T	$\frac{3}{8}$	.03	.11	.20	.28	.36	.45	.53	.61	.70	.78	.86	.95
I	$\frac{1}{2}$	.04	.13*	.21	.29	.38*	.46	.54	.63*	.71	.79	.88*	.96
O	$\frac{5}{8}$	.05	.14	.22	.30	.39	.47	.55	.64	.72	.80	.89	.97
N	$\frac{3}{4}$	.06	.15	.23	.31	.40	.48	.56	.65	.73	.81	.90	.98
S	$\frac{7}{8}$	.07	.16	.24	.32	.41	.49	.57	.66	.74	.82	.91	.99

* accounts for the $\frac{4}{100}$"s

Look at the shaded column on the left titled FRACTIONS. Notice that eighths are used. Although not perfectly accurate, $\frac{1}{8}$" is widely accepted as equal to $\frac{1}{100}$ of a foot.

$$\frac{1}{8}" = \frac{1}{100}" = 0.01"$$

Eighths are used because they are the closest to a hundred units in 12". There are 8 eighths in one inch. There are 96 eighths in 12".

Notice there are $\frac{4}{100}$" missing. The missing $\frac{4}{100}$" is accounted for evenly over the Decimals of a Foot Conversion Table: .13, .38, .63, .88.

Example 1:

What is the decimal of a foot equivalent for $\frac{5}{8}$"? $\frac{5}{8}$" = _0.05'_

Locate the fractions row titled $\frac{5}{8}$.

Locate the inches. There are no full inches so locate the column titled **0**.

INCHES

FRACTIONS	0	1	2	3	4	5	6	7	8	9	10	11
0	.00	.08	.17	.25	.33	.42	.50	.58	.67	.75	.83	.92
$\frac{1}{8}$	.01	.09	.18	.26	.34	.43	.51	.59	.68	.76	.84	.93
$\frac{1}{4}$	.02	.10	.19	.27	.35	.44	.52	.60	.69	.77	.85	.94
$\frac{3}{8}$	.03	.11	.20	.28	.36	.45	.53	.61	.70	.78	.86	.95
$\frac{1}{2}$	.04	.13*	.21	.29	.38*	.46	.54	.63*	.71	.79	.88*	.96
$\frac{5}{8}$	**.05**	.14	.22	.30	.39	.47	.55	.64	.72	.80	.89	.97
$\frac{3}{4}$	.06	.15	.23	.31	.40	.48	.56	.65	.73	.81	.90	.98
$\frac{7}{8}$	.07	.16	.24	.32	.41	.49	.57	.66	.74	.82	.91	.99

Example 2:

What is the decimal of a foot equivalent for $10\frac{3}{4}$"?

$10\frac{3}{4}$" = _0.90'_

Locate the fractions row titled $\frac{3}{4}$. Locate the inches column titled 10.

INCHES

FRACTIONS	0	1	2	3	4	5	6	7	8	9	10	11
0	.00	.08	.17	.25	.33	.42	.50	.58	.67	.75	.83	.92
$\frac{1}{8}$	.01	.09	.18	.26	.34	.43	.51	.59	.68	.76	.84	.93
$\frac{1}{4}$	.02	.10	.19	.27	.35	.44	.52	.60	.69	.77	.85	.94
$\frac{3}{8}$	.03	.11	.20	.28	.36	.45	.53	.61	.70	.78	.86	.95
$\frac{1}{2}$	.04	.13*	.21	.29	.38*	.46	.54	.63*	.71	.79	.88*	.96
$\frac{5}{8}$	.05	.14	.22	.30	.39	.47	.55	.64	.72	.80	.89	.97
$\frac{3}{4}$	.06	.15	.23	.31	.40	.48	.56	.65	.73	.81	**.90**	.98
$\frac{7}{8}$	.07	.16	.24	.32	.41	.49	.57	.66	.74	.82	.91	.99

Write the decimal of a foot equivalent. Use the Decimals of a Foot Conversion Table.

1) $\frac{3}{4}{}'' =$

2) $1\frac{5}{8}{}'' =$

3) $6\frac{1}{8}{}'' =$

4) $12'' =$

5) $8\frac{3}{8}{}'' =$

6) $6'' =$

7) $7\frac{7}{8}{}'' =$

8) $3\frac{3}{4}{}'' =$

9) $1\frac{4}{16}{}'' =$

10) $9\frac{10}{16}{}'' =$

Quick Conversion Method

Although the conversion chart is a reliable means of converting fractions to decimals and decimals to fractions, it is impractical to carry around all the time.

The Quick Conversion Method converts inches and fractions of an inch to decimals of a foot by adding or subtracting eighths (.01')

Fractions of an Inch to Decimals of a Foot

Fraction	Decimal of a Foot
$\frac{1}{8}{}''$	.01'
$\frac{1}{4}{}''$	.02'
$\frac{3}{8}{}''$	.03'
$\frac{1}{2}{}''$	.04'
$\frac{5}{8}{}''$	.05'
$\frac{3}{4}{}''$	.06'
$\frac{7}{8}{}''$	.07'
$1''$	.08'

Note: ruler below is not to scale.

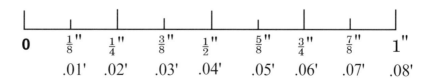

Inches to Decimals of a Foot

Inch	Decimal of a Foot
1"	.08'
2"	.17'
3"	.25'
4"	.33'
5"	.42'
6"	.50'
7"	.58'
8"	.67'
9"	.75'
10"	.83'
11"	.92'
12"	1.00'

Note: ruler below is not to scale.

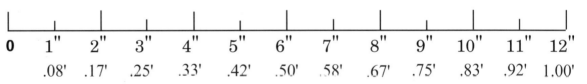

0	1"	2"	3"	4"	5"	6"	7"	8"	9"	10"	11"	12"
	.08'	.17'	.25'	.33'	.42'	.50'	.58'	.67'	.75'	.83'	.92'	1.00'

Note: Avoid using .17', .33' .67' and .83' when using the quick conversion method.

These are repeating decimals that make up the missing $\frac{4}{100}$ ths between 96 eighths and 100 hundredths.

Example 1:

Adding

Convert $5\frac{1}{2}"$ to a decimal of a foot.

$5" = .42'$ Locate inches in the table *Inches to decimals of a Foot.*

$+ \ \frac{1}{2}" = .04'$ Locate fractions in the table *Fractions of an Inch to Decimals of a Foot.*

$\overline{5\frac{1}{2}" = .46'}$

Add the decimals.

Example 2:

Subtracting

Convert $9\frac{1}{4}$" to a decimal of a foot.

$9" = .75'$ Locate inches in the table *Inches to decimals of a Foot.*

$-\frac{1}{4}" = .02'$ Locate fractions in the table *Fractions of an Inch to Decimals of a Foot.*

$8\frac{3}{4}" = .73'$

Subtract the decimals.

Convert the following from feet, inches and fractions to feet and decimals of a foot.

 1) $9'\ 9\frac{1}{2}"$ 2) $3'\ 3\frac{3}{8}"$  3) $6'\ 11\frac{1}{8}"$ 4) $1'\ 0\frac{5}{8}"$

5) $25'\ 4\frac{7}{8}"$ 6) $16'\ 5\frac{3}{4}"$ 7) $12'\ 1\frac{1}{4}"$ 8) $1'\ 6\frac{1}{4}"$

Convert feet and decimals of a foot to feet, inches and fractions.

1) 7.28'   2)   6.56'   3)   26.60'   4)   2.95'

5) 42.23'   6)   12.51'   7)   13.15'   8)   0.80'

PRACTICE

1) A trades worker buys a hammer for $18.00, a box of nails for $18.72, glue for $6.92 and a chisel for $13.77. Calculate the total.

2) Calculate the total number of board feet for the following list of materials.
Studs 650.57 board feet
Plates 312.75 board feet
Braces 134.25 board feet

3) An apprentice glues 12 pieces of wood together, side by side. Each piece of wood is 0.038 m wide. Calculate the width of the new piece.

4) A tank holds 31.25 L. Fuel is 0.825 dollars per litre. Calculate the cost of the fuel.

5) A sheet of 0.019 m plywood is made up of 5 layers of equal thickness. Calculate the thickness of each layer.

6) A hammer that usually sells for $18.25 is reduced $1.99 in price. What is the new price?

7) The pieces shown below were glued together to form a chopping block. What is the total width of the block?

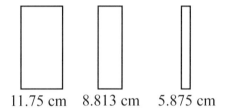

11.75 cm   8.813 cm   5.875 cm

8) Calculate the difference in length between two boards that measure 4.877 m and 3.658 m.

9) On Tuesday, a crew poured 36.482 m³ of concrete.
On Wednesday, the crew poured 27.595 m³ of concrete.

    a) Calculate the total the crew poured in two days. Round your answer to the nearest hundredth.

    b) How much more did the crew pour on Tuesday than Wednesday? Round your answer to the nearest hundredth.

10) Calculate the total distance around the figure shown below.

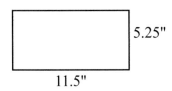

5.25"

11.5"

11) An apprentice cut a piece 0.058 m long from a sheet of drywall that measures 2.440 m long. Calculate the length of the remaining piece of drywall.

12) There are 6 risers in a staircase that has a total rise of 1.146 m. What is the height of 1 riser?

13) Thirty-one sheets of plywood cost $482.36.

    a) Calculate the cost of one sheet of plywood.

    b) Calculate the cost of 8 sheets of plywood.

14) The first floor of a building is 0.415 m above grade. The first storey is 3.104 m, the second storey is 2.9 m and the third storey, to the top of the roof, is 3.519 m. What is the total height of the building?

15) It took 13.362 m³ of concrete to make 17 identical footings. How much concrete did it take to make one footing?

16) The total run of a staircase that has five treads is 1.195 m. Calculate the width of one tread.

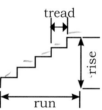

17) A contractor buys 103 hinges at $0.39 each. What is the total cost?

18) The distance between rungs, measured centre to centre, on a ladder is .305 m. What is the distance from the ground to the top of the 13th rung?

19) A contractor purchases lumber at $1.97 per board foot.

    a)   Calculate the cost of 2 board feet.

    b)   Calculate the cost of 1.667 board feet.

    c)   Calculate the cost of 32.5 board feet.

20) An apprentice is paid $16.82/hr. How much does the apprentice earn in a 37.5 hour work week?

INTRODUCTION

Trades workers use fractions all the time to measure materials and read blueprints.

When you have completed this section you will be able to:

- ❑ Change improper fractions to mixed numbers and mixed numbers to improper fractions.
- ❑ Choose a common denominator.
- ❑ Express fractions in lowest terms.
- ❑ Multiply and divide fractions.
- ❑ Add and subtract fractions.
- ❑ Solve word problems using fractions.
- ❑ Solve applications using fractions.

DEFINING FRACTIONS

The following definitions will help you to understand and to use fractions better.

Whole Number: Whole numbers are used to count things.
Examples: 1, 2, 3, 4, and so on.

Fraction: A fraction is a ratio of two numbers written with an oblique or horizontal bar.

> Example: 1/2 or $\frac{1}{2}$
>
> 1 ⟵ numerator, the number of parts
>
> 2 ⟵ denominator, the whole amount

The numbers 1 and 2 in the fraction are called terms.

Proper Fraction: A proper fraction is a part of a whole. It is less than one. The numerator (top) is smaller than the denominator (bottom).

> Example: $\frac{1}{2}, \frac{7}{8}, \frac{3}{4}$

Improper Fraction: An improper fraction has a numerator that is bigger than its denominator. An improper fraction has a value equal to or greater than one.

> Example: $\frac{9}{8}, \frac{14}{4}, \frac{8}{7}, \frac{3}{2}$

Mixed Numbers: A mixed number is a combination of a whole number and a fraction.

> Example: $2\frac{1}{4}, 5\frac{1}{3}, 3\frac{7}{8}$

Equivalent Fraction: Equivalent fractions are fractions that have the same value.

> Example: $\frac{1}{4} = \frac{2}{8} = \frac{4}{16}$

Lowest Term: The lowest term means reducing the fraction to the lowest equivalent fraction.

> Example: $\frac{2}{4} = \frac{1}{2}$ $\frac{2}{8} = \frac{1}{4}$

Write whole number, proper fraction, improper fraction or mixed number beside each of the following.

1) $\frac{1}{2}$ 2) $3\frac{1}{4}$ 3) $\frac{3}{2}$ 4) 7

5) $\frac{1}{4}$ 6) $2\frac{1}{16}$ 7) $\frac{7}{8}$ 8) $\frac{13}{8}$

9) $\frac{2}{1}$ 10) 16 11) $\frac{12}{16}$ 12) $\frac{1}{4}$

13) $1\frac{1}{4}$ 14) $\frac{5}{4}$ 15) $\frac{9}{8}$ 16) $1\frac{1}{8}$

WRITING FRACTIONS

numerator $\Longleftarrow 1 \Longrightarrow$ number of pieces you are counting
denominator $\Longleftarrow \overline{2} \Longrightarrow$ the name of the whole

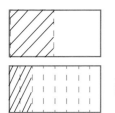 $\frac{1}{2}$  $\frac{1}{4}$ 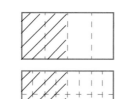 $\frac{2}{4}$ $\frac{3}{4}$

$\frac{2}{8}$ $\frac{4}{8}$ $\frac{8}{16}$ $\frac{12}{16}$

Write the fraction that represents the shaded portion of each of the following sheets of plywood:

1)    2)    3) 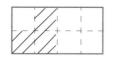   4)

5)    6)    7) 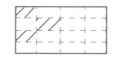   8)

CHANGING IMPROPER FRACTIONS TO MIXED NUMBERS

Improper fractions should always be changed to whole or mixed numbers.

Step 1:   Divide the numerator by the denominator.

Step 2:   Write the remainder over the denominator.

Step 3:   Write the whole number beside the fraction.

Step 4:   Express fractions in lowest terms.

Example 1:

Change $\frac{34}{8}$ to a whole or mixed number.

$$8\overline{)34} \quad \begin{array}{l} 4 \\ \underline{32} \\ 2 \end{array}$$

There is a remainder. Write the remainder over the denominator.

$\frac{34}{8} = 4\frac{2}{8} = 4\frac{1}{4}$ Reduce fraction to lowest terms.

Example 2:

Change $\frac{12}{4}$ to a whole or mixed number.

$$4\overline{)12} \quad \begin{array}{l} 3 \\ \underline{12} \\ 0 \end{array}$$

There is no remainder.

$\frac{12}{4} = 3$

Change the following improper fractions to whole or mixed numbers.

1) $\frac{4}{2}$ 2) $\frac{10}{8}$ 3) $\frac{8}{4}$ 4) $\frac{15}{5}$

5) $\frac{4}{3}$ 6) $\frac{10}{4}$ 7) $\frac{3}{2}$ 8) $\frac{5}{2}$

9) $\frac{13}{8}$ 10) $\frac{21}{3}$ 11) $\frac{7}{4}$ 12) $\frac{9}{3}$

13) $\frac{5}{4}$ 14) $\frac{7}{2}$ 15) $\frac{17}{16}$ 16) $\frac{21}{16}$

CHANGING MIXED NUMBERS TO IMPROPER FRACTIONS

When you multiply and divide fractions, you need to change mixed numbers to improper fractions.

Step 1:   Multiply the whole number by the denominator.

Step 2:   Add the numerator.

Step 3:   Write the total over the denominator.

Example 1:

Change $2\frac{3}{8}$ to an improper fraction.

$$2 \times \frac{3}{8} + = \frac{19}{8}$$

CHANGING A WHOLE NUMBER TO AN IMPROPER FRACTION

Example:

Place the whole number over 1. $3 = \frac{3}{1}$

Change the following mixed numbers to improper fractions.

1) $1\frac{1}{2}$ 2) $1\frac{1}{3}$ 3) $2\frac{1}{4}$ 4) $3\frac{1}{8}$

5) 4 6) $7\frac{1}{2}$ 7) $3\frac{3}{4}$ 8) $6\frac{3}{16}$

9) 11 10) $9\frac{11}{16}$ 11) $4\frac{5}{8}$ 12) $3\frac{3}{8}$

13) $2\frac{1}{8}$ 14) $9\frac{1}{3}$ 15) 21 16) $6\frac{7}{8}$

Remember:

You multiply the numerator and the denominator by the same number.

COMMON DENOMINATORS

When you add and subtract fractions, the fractions must have a common denominator. This means all fractions in the problem have the same denominator. A common denominator is a number that can be divided into evenly by all the denominators in the problem. The smallest number that can be used as the denominator is called the lowest common denominator (LCD).

Step 1: Multiply the numerator and the denominator by the same number.

Example 1:

$$\frac{1}{2} =$$

$$\frac{1 \times 2}{2 \times 2} = \frac{2}{4}$$ Multiply the numerator and the denominator by the same number.

$$\frac{1}{2} = \frac{2}{4}$$ These are equivalent fractions.

Example 2:

$$\frac{1}{4} =$$

$$\frac{1 \times 4}{4 \times 4} = \frac{4}{16}$$ Multiply the numerator and the denominator by the same number.

$$\frac{1}{4} = \frac{4}{16}$$ These are equivalent fractions.

Show the following pairs of fractions are equivalent fractions by dividing up the sheets of plywood.

1) $\frac{3}{4} = \frac{6}{8}$　　2) $\frac{1}{2} = \frac{4}{8}$　　3) $\frac{1}{3} = \frac{2}{6}$

4) $\frac{1}{4} = \frac{2}{8}$　　5) $\frac{3}{4} = \frac{12}{16}$

Find the LCD for the following pairs of fractions.

1) $\frac{1}{4}$, $\frac{1}{2}$

2) $\frac{1}{8}$, $\frac{1}{4}$

3) $\frac{1}{3}$, $\frac{1}{12}$

4) $\frac{3}{8}$, $\frac{5}{16}$

5) $\frac{1}{5}$, $\frac{1}{2}$

6) $\frac{3}{4}$, $\frac{7}{8}$

7) $\frac{1}{2}$, $\frac{1}{3}$

8) $\frac{1}{12}$, $\frac{1}{8}$

9) $\frac{2}{3}$, $\frac{3}{4}$

10) $\frac{5}{8}$, $\frac{7}{16}$

11) $\frac{3}{4}$, $\frac{2}{5}$

12) $\frac{1}{20}$, $\frac{3}{5}$

13) $\frac{5}{8}$, $\frac{1}{2}$

14) $\frac{3}{4}$, $\frac{11}{16}$

15) $\frac{2}{6}$, $\frac{3}{8}$

16) $\frac{3}{8}$, $\frac{15}{16}$

Hint:
The denominator
for any whole
number is one.

$4 = \frac{4}{1}$ $8 = \frac{8}{1}$

MULTIPLYING FRACTIONS

MULTIPLYING FRACTIONS

Step 1:   Change all mixed numbers and
whole numbers to improper fractions.

Step 2:   Multiply the numerators.
Multiply the denominators.

Step 3:   Change improper fractions to mixed numbers.
Reduce fractions to lowest terms.

Example 1:

$\frac{1}{2} \times \frac{1}{2} = \frac{1}{4}$

There are no mixed numbers.
Multiply the numerators.
Multiply the denominators.

Example 2:

$1\frac{1}{2} \times 2\frac{1}{4} =$ $\frac{3}{2} \times \frac{9}{4} =$ $\frac{27}{8} = 3\frac{3}{8}$

Change mixed numbers to
improper fractions.
Multiply the numerators.
Multiply the denominators.

Change improper
fractions to mixed
fractions.

Multiply the following.

1) $\frac{1}{4} \times \frac{1}{3}$ 2) $\frac{2}{5} \times \frac{1}{3}$ 3) $\frac{1}{4} \times \frac{2}{3}$ 4) $\frac{7}{8} \times \frac{1}{5}$

5) $2 \times \frac{1}{4}$ 6) $5 \times \frac{1}{3}$ 7) $\frac{1}{2} \times 9$ 8) $\frac{2}{3} \times 4$

9) $1\frac{2}{3} \times 4$ 10) $2\frac{4}{5} \times 3$ 11) $2 \times 9\frac{1}{4}$ 12) $2 \times 1\frac{3}{4}$

13) $3\frac{1}{3} \times 1\frac{1}{8}$ 14) $1\frac{5}{8} \times 3\frac{1}{4}$ 15) $1\frac{1}{8} \times 1\frac{1}{4}$ 16) $2\frac{1}{2} \times 4\frac{1}{3}$

17) $6\frac{2}{3} \times 1\frac{1}{4}$ 18) $1\frac{1}{2} \times 3\frac{1}{2}$ 19) $7\frac{1}{8} \times 4\frac{1}{4}$ 20) $3\frac{3}{16} \times 2\frac{1}{2}$

DIVIDING FRACTIONS

INVERTING FRACTIONS

Example:

$\frac{8}{5}$ is called the inverse or reciprocal of $\frac{5}{8}$.

$\frac{4}{3}$ is called the inverse or reciprocal of $\frac{3}{4}$.

INVERTING MIXED NUMBERS AND WHOLE NUMBERS

Step 1: Change mixed or whole numbers to improper fractions.

Step 2: Invert the proper fraction.

Example:

$2\frac{1}{4} = \frac{9}{4}$ The inverse of $\frac{9}{4}$ is $\frac{4}{9}$.

$7 = \frac{7}{1}$ The inverse of $\frac{7}{1}$ is $\frac{1}{7}$.

Write the inverse of the following.

1) $\frac{7}{8}$ 2) $\frac{3}{4}$ 3) $\frac{2}{1}$ 4) $\frac{2}{3}$

5) $\frac{9}{2}$ 6) $\frac{7}{4}$ 7) $\frac{3}{8}$ 8) $\frac{5}{8}$

9) $1\frac{1}{2}$ 10) $2\frac{3}{16}$ 11) $6\frac{5}{8}$ 12) $3\frac{3}{4}$

13) $5\frac{1}{4}$ 14) $8\frac{9}{16}$ 15) $4\frac{3}{4}$ 16) $7\frac{1}{2}$

DIVIDING FRACTIONS

Step 1:   Change all mixed numbers and whole numbers to improper fractions.

Step 2:   Change the division sign to a multiplication sign. Invert the second fraction.

Step 3:   Multiply the numerator by the numerator. Multiply the denominator by the denominator.

Step 4:   Change improper fractions to mixed numbers or whole numbers. Express fractions in lowest terms.

Example 1:

$\frac{1}{2} \div \frac{1}{4} =$ There are no mixed numbers.

$\frac{1}{2} \times \frac{4}{1} =$ Change the division sign to a multiplication sign. Invert the second fraction.

$\frac{1}{2} \times \frac{4}{1} = \frac{4}{2}$ Multiply the numerator by the numerator. Multiply the denominator by the denominator.

$\frac{4}{2} = 2$ Change improper fractions to mixed numbers or whole numbers.

Example 2:

$2\frac{1}{2} \div 1\frac{1}{4} = \frac{5}{2} \div \frac{5}{4} =$ Change mixed numbers and whole numbers to improper fractions.

$\frac{5}{2} \times \frac{4}{5} =$ Change the division sign to a multiplication sign. Invert the second fraction.

$\frac{5}{2} \times \frac{4}{5} = \frac{20}{10}$ Multiply the numerator by the numerator. Multiply the denominator by the denominator.

$\frac{20}{10} = 2$ Change improper fractions to mixed numbers or whole numbers.

Divide the following.

1) $\frac{1}{3} \div \frac{1}{2}$

2) $\frac{2}{5} \div \frac{1}{2}$

3) $\frac{1}{4} \div \frac{1}{3}$

4) $\frac{2}{3} \div \frac{3}{4}$

5) $\frac{3}{7} \div \frac{4}{9}$

6) $\frac{2}{11} \div \frac{5}{8}$

7) $\frac{1}{3} \div \frac{2}{3}$

8) $\frac{5}{16} \div \frac{2}{3}$

9) $7\frac{1}{2} \div \frac{1}{3}$

10) $6 \div \frac{2}{3}$

11) $3 \div \frac{7}{4}$

12) $\frac{2}{3} \div 4$

13) $\frac{1}{16} \div 1\frac{1}{8}$

14) $2\frac{2}{3} \div 4$

15) $1\frac{1}{5} \div 3$

16) $2\frac{3}{8} \div 1$

17) $7\frac{1}{2} \div 3\frac{1}{2}$

18) $1\frac{1}{4} \div 2\frac{3}{8}$

19) $1\frac{1}{8} \div 2\frac{2}{3}$

20) $2\frac{5}{8} \div 2\frac{3}{8}$

ADDING FRACTIONS

Step 1: Determine the common denominator.
Do not change mixed numbers or whole numbers to improper fractions.

Step 2: Add the numerators and place the answer over the denominator. Do not add the denominators.
Add the whole numbers.

Step 3: Express fractions in lowest terms.

Example 1:

$$\frac{1}{4} + \frac{1}{4} = \frac{2}{4}$$

There is already a common denominator. Add the numerators and place the answer over the denominator.

$$\frac{2}{4} = \frac{1}{2}$$

Express fractions in lowest terms.

Example 2:

$$\frac{1}{2} + \frac{3}{8} =$$

Determine the common denominator. The lowest common denominator (LCD) for 2 and 8 is 8.

$$\frac{1 \times 4}{2 \times 4} = \frac{4}{8}$$

Change $\frac{1}{2}$ to eighths. Multiply the numerator and the denominator by 4.

$$\frac{4}{8} + \frac{3}{8} = \frac{7}{8}$$

Add the numerators. Do not add the denominators.

$$\frac{7}{8}$$

Express fractions in lowest terms. Seven-eighths cannot be reduced.

Example 3:

$$1\frac{3}{4} + 2\frac{5}{8} =$$

Determine the common denominator.

$$1\frac{3 \times 2}{4 \times 2} = 1\frac{6}{8}$$

The LCD for 4 and 8 is 8.

$$1\frac{6}{8} + 2\frac{5}{8} = 3\frac{11}{8}$$

Add the numerators and place the answer over the denominator. Do not add the denominators. Add the whole numbers.

$$3\frac{11}{8} = 4\frac{3}{8}$$

Express fractions in lowest terms.

Example 4:

$$1\frac{2}{3} + 3\frac{3}{4} =$$

Determine the common denominator.

$$1\frac{2 \times 4}{3 \times 4} = 1\frac{8}{12}$$

The LCD for 3 and 4 is 12.

$$3\frac{3 \times 3}{4 \times 3} = 3\frac{9}{12}$$

$$1\frac{8}{12} + 3\frac{9}{12} = 4\frac{17}{12}$$

Add the numerators and place the answer over the denominator. Do not add the denominators. Add the whole numbers.

$$4\frac{17}{12} = 5\frac{5}{12}$$

Express fractions in lowest terms.

Add the following.

1) $\frac{1}{4} + \frac{2}{4}$

2) $\frac{1}{4} + \frac{3}{4}$

3) $\frac{3}{8} + \frac{1}{8}$

4) $\frac{5}{8} + \frac{7}{8}$

5) $\frac{1}{2} + \frac{1}{4}$

6) $\frac{1}{2} + \frac{1}{3}$

7) $\frac{3}{6} + \frac{2}{6}$

8) $\frac{1}{4} + \frac{3}{8}$

9) $\frac{5}{8} + \frac{13}{16}$

10) $\frac{5}{6} + \frac{1}{4}$

11) $\frac{1}{4} + \frac{7}{8}$

12) $\frac{5}{16} + \frac{3}{4}$

13) $7\frac{1}{8} + 6\frac{1}{8}$

14) $6\frac{1}{8} + 4\frac{3}{16}$

15) $2\frac{1}{2} + 1\frac{1}{4}$

16) $5\frac{1}{3} + 7\frac{1}{6}$

17) $3 + 7\frac{1}{8} + 5\frac{5}{8}$

18) $2\frac{1}{16} + 3\frac{1}{8} + 7\frac{7}{16}$

19) $2\frac{1}{4} + 4\frac{1}{2} + 5\frac{7}{16}$

20) $3\frac{1}{4} + 9\frac{3}{8} + 1\frac{3}{4}$

SUBTRACTING FRACTIONS

Step 1: Determine the common denominator. Do not change mixed numbers or whole numbers to improper fractions.

Step 2: Subtract the numerators and place the answer over the denominator. Do not subtract the denominators. Subtract the whole numbers.

Step 3: Express fractions in lowest terms.

Example 1:

$$\frac{3}{4} - \frac{1}{4} = \frac{2}{4}$$

$$\frac{2}{4} = \frac{1}{2}$$

There is already a common denominator. Subtract the numerators and place the answer over the denominator.

Express fractions in lowest terms.

Example 2:

$$\frac{3}{4} - \frac{5}{8} =$$

Determine the common denominator.

$$\frac{3 \times 2}{4 \times 2} = \frac{6}{8}$$

The LCD for 4 and 8 is 8.

$$\frac{6}{8} - \frac{5}{8} = \frac{1}{8}$$

Subtract the numerators and place the answer over the denominator. Do not subtract the denominators.

$$\frac{1}{8}$$

Express fractions in lowest terms. $\frac{1}{8}$ is the lowest term.

Example 3:

$$4\frac{5}{8} - 2\frac{3}{16} =$$

Determine the common denominator.

$$4\frac{5 \times 2}{8 \times 2} = 4\frac{10}{16}$$

The LCD for 8 and 16 is 16.

$$4\frac{10}{16} - 2\frac{3}{16} = 2\frac{7}{16}$$

Subtract the numerators and place the answer over the denominator. Do not subtract the denominators. Subtract the whole numbers.

$$2\frac{7}{16}$$

Express fractions in lowest terms. $2\frac{7}{16}$ is the lowest term.

Example 4:

Sometimes when you subtract fractions you have to borrow just like with whole numbers.

$7\frac{1}{4} - 1\frac{3}{4} =$

There is already a common denominator.
$\frac{3}{4}$ is bigger than $\frac{1}{4}$.
You have to borrow from 7.

$7\frac{1}{4} = 6\frac{5}{4}$

Borrow 1 from 7 and change the 7 to 6.
Change the borrowed 1 to fourths.
$1 = \frac{4}{4}$. Add $\frac{4}{4}$ to $\frac{1}{4}$.

$6\frac{5}{4} - 1\frac{3}{4} = 5\frac{2}{4}$

Subtract the numerators and place the answer over the denominator.
Do not subtract the denominators. Subtract the whole numbers.

$5\frac{2}{4} = 5\frac{1}{2}$

Express fractions in lowest terms.

Example 5:

$5\frac{3}{8} - 1\frac{3}{4} =$

Determine the common denominator.

$1\frac{3 \times 2}{4 \times 2} = 1\frac{6}{8}$

The LCD for 8 and 4 is 8.

$5\frac{3}{8} - 1\frac{6}{8} =$

$\frac{6}{8}$ is bigger than $\frac{3}{8}$.
You have to borrow from 5.

$5\frac{3}{8} = 4\frac{11}{8}$

Borrow 1 from 5 and change the five to 4.
Change the borrowed 1 to eighths.
$1 = \frac{8}{8}$. Add $\frac{8}{8}$ to $\frac{3}{8}$.

$4\frac{11}{8} - 1\frac{6}{8} = 3\frac{5}{8}$

Subtract the numerators and place the answer over the denominator. Do not subtract the denominators. Subtract the whole numbers.

$3\frac{5}{8}$

Express fractions in lowest terms.
$3\frac{5}{8}$ is the lowest term.

Subtract the following.

1) $\frac{3}{4} - \frac{1}{4}$

2) $\frac{3}{8} - \frac{1}{8}$

3) $\frac{15}{16} - \frac{7}{16}$

4) $\frac{7}{8} - \frac{3}{8}$

5) $\frac{3}{4} - \frac{1}{2}$

6) $\frac{1}{2} - \frac{1}{3}$

7) $\frac{3}{8} - \frac{1}{4}$

8) $\frac{11}{16} - \frac{3}{8}$

9) $4\frac{7}{8} - 2\frac{2}{8}$

10) $5\frac{5}{8} - 1\frac{5}{16}$

11) $3\frac{2}{3} - 1\frac{1}{2}$

12) $4\frac{3}{8} - 1\frac{1}{4}$

13) $3\frac{1}{4} - 1\frac{3}{4}$

14) $12\frac{3}{8} - 5\frac{5}{8}$

15) $2\frac{1}{4} - 1\frac{1}{2}$

16) $2\frac{1}{2} - \frac{3}{4}$

17) $5 - 1\frac{3}{4}$

18) $1 - \frac{5}{8}$

19) $7 - \frac{15}{16}$

20) $6 - 4\frac{1}{8}$

21) $7\frac{5}{8} - 2\frac{3}{4}$

22) $15\frac{1}{4} - 13\frac{5}{16}$

23) $2\frac{1}{5} - 1\frac{1}{10}$

24) $3\frac{5}{8} - 1\frac{3}{4}$

PRACTICE

Remember:

Always reduce
fractions to the
lowest terms.

1) A carpenter takes one day to complete $\frac{1}{2}$ a set of cabinets. What fraction is complete in $\frac{1}{4}$ of a day?

2) A sheet of drywall is cut into quarters. Each quarter is cut into thirds. What fraction of a whole sheet is each of these small pieces?

3) A chopping block was made by gluing boards $3\frac{1}{4}"$, $6\frac{1}{8}"$ and $2\frac{5}{16}"$ wide together. What is the total width of the chopping block?

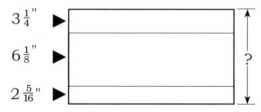

4) It takes $4\frac{1}{4}$ sheets of 8' long plywood laid out end to end to cover a roof. How long is the roof?

5) A trades worker uses $1\frac{1}{2}"$ stock to temporarily shim up a heavy beam. One shim is $1\frac{1}{2}"$ thick. How many shims or pieces must the carpenter use to lift the beam $7\frac{1}{2}"$?

6) $\frac{5}{8}$" plywood is nailed to $9\frac{1}{4}$" joists that rest on a beam that is $11\frac{3}{8}$" deep. What is the total distance from the bottom of the beam to the top of the plywood flooring?

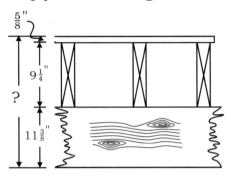

Use the drawing below to answer the next 4 questions.

7) What does distance A equal?

distance A is _____

8) What does distance B equal?

distance B is _____

9) What does distance C equal?

distance C is _____

10) What does distance D equal?

distance D is _____

11) Calculate the missing dimension in the drawing below.

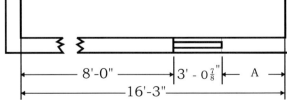

12) There are 13 risers in a staircase. What is the total rise (height) of the staircase if each riser is $7\frac{3}{8}"$?

13) How many sheets of $\frac{5}{8}"$ plywood are there in a stack

    a) 15" high   b) $8\frac{1}{8}"$ high

14) Calculate the missing dimension (B) in the drawing below:

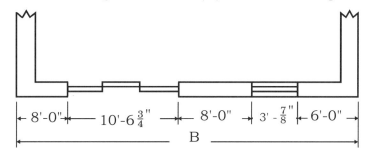

8'-0"   10'-6$\frac{3}{4}$"   8'-0"   3'-$\frac{7}{8}$"   6'-0"

B

15) An apprentice cuts a piece of stock into 4 pieces. The lengths are $3\frac{3}{8}"$, $2\frac{7}{16}"$, $4\frac{1}{2}"$ and $1\frac{1}{4}"$. If $\frac{1}{8}"$ is used up for each kerf (saw cut), what was the original length of the board?

Hint:

There were 3 kerfs made in cutting the board.

16) A steel post $103\frac{3}{16}"$ high is bolted to the top of a concrete pier that is $10\frac{1}{4}"$ high. The pier sits on top of a footing $12\frac{3}{4}"$ thick. What is the total distance from the bottom of the footing to the top of the post?

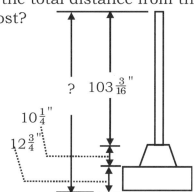

17) How thick would a stack of 7 sheets of $\frac{3}{8}$" plywood be?

18) An apprentice divides a 4'–10" storey pole into eight equal spaces. What is the length of each space? Hint: Convert feet to inches.

19) On a scaled drawing where $\frac{1}{8}$" is equal to 1' 0", how many feet would $7\frac{3}{8}$" represent?

20) A floor is covered with flooring strips $2\frac{1}{3}$" wide. How many strips are needed to cover a floor 117" wide?

21) Three boards, $5\frac{3}{8}$", $2\frac{1}{16}$" and $3\frac{5}{8}$" wide are glued together. What is the width of the resulting board?

22) The blueprint framing specifications state that the maximum size diameter hole that can be drilled into the centre of a joist at mid span is $\frac{1}{4}$ of the joist depth. What would the maximum size hole be for joist that is $9\frac{1}{4}$" deep?

23) The concrete specifications state that the maximum size of aggregate for a wall form is $\frac{1}{5}$ of the narrowest dimension between the sides of the forms. What would the maximum size aggregate be for an 8" thick concrete wall?

INTRODUCTION

Trades workers use percent to calculate proportions of mixtures and discounts and increases for equipment and material purchases or rentals. Percent is also used to calculate wages, taxes, and increases or decreases in production.

When you have completed this chapter you will be able to:

- ❐ Convert between fractions, decimals and percentages.
- ❐ Calculate percentage increases and decreases.
- ❐ Solve percentage word problems.
- ❐ Solve applications using percent.

WHAT IS PERCENT?

Percent is used to calculate interest, mark-up, discounts and tax rates. Trades Workers use percent to calculate proportions of mixtures, waste, swell factors and shrink factors.

Percent means per hundred and is a ratio that expresses a quantity out of one hundred. It is shown by the sign %.

Hint:

Percent is similar to "decimals of a foot", working to two decimal places. Example: 7" = .58" or 58% of 12"

Example :

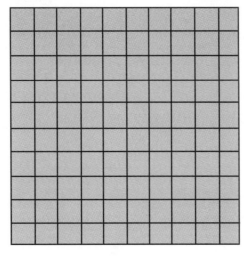

100% = 1 hundred parts
or one whole object

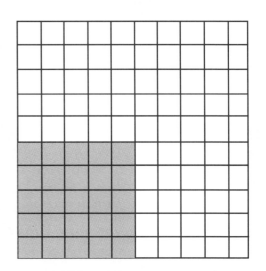

25% = 25 parts out of
a hundred

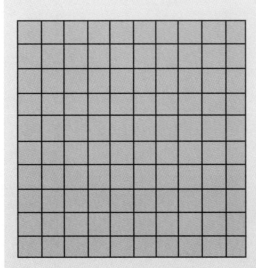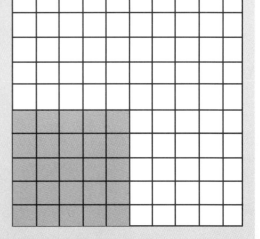

125% = 1 one whole object and 25 parts of another

CONVERTING BETWEEN PERCENTS, DECIMALS AND FRACTIONS

To make it easier to use your calculator and perform percent calculations, you need to know how to convert between percents, decimals and fractions.

Percent has the same value as:
- a decimal with two places (hundredths)
  $25\% = .25$

- a fraction with a denominator of 100
  $25\% = \frac{25}{100}$

CONVERTING PERCENTS TO DECIMALS

Step 1:   Convert fractions to decimals.

Step 2:   Drop the % symbol.

Step 3:   Move the decimal point 2 places to the left.

Example 1:

Change 19% to a decimal.

$19\% = 19$ Drop the % symbol.

$19 = 0.19$ Move the decimal point 2 places to the left.

Example 2:

Change 16.2% to a decimal.

$16.2\% = 16.2$ Drop the % symbol.

$16.2 = 0.162$ Move the decimal point 2 places to the left.

Example 3:

Change 3% to a decimal.

$3\% = 3$ Drop the % symbol.

$3 = 0.03$ Move the decimal point 2 places to the left.

Example 4:
Convert 127% to a decimal.

127% = 127   Drop the % symbol.

127 = 1.27   Move the decimal point 2 places to the left.

Example 5:
Convert $22\frac{1}{2}$% to a decimal.

$22\frac{1}{2}$% = 22.5%   Convert fractions to decimals.

22.5% = 22.5   Drop the % symbol.

22.5 = 0.225   Move the decimal point 2 places to the left.

Example 6:
Convert $\frac{1}{4}$% to a decimal.

$\frac{1}{4}$% = 0.25%   Convert fractions to decimals.

.25% = 0.25   Drop the % symbol.

0.25 = 0.0025 Move the decimal point 2 places to the left.

Convert the following percent to decimals.

1)   18%

2)   25%

3)   32%

4)   88%

5)   6%

6)   3%

7)   9%

8)   13.8%

9)   21.6%

10)   74.51%

11)   100%

12)   200%

13) $2\frac{1}{2}$%

14) $26\frac{1}{4}$%

15) $36\frac{1}{4}$%

16) $18\frac{7}{10}$%

17) $215\frac{1}{2}$%

18) $9\frac{1}{4}$%

19) $122\frac{3}{4}$%

20) $2\frac{4}{5}$%

CONVERTING DECIMALS TO PERCENTS

Step 1:   Move the decimal point two places to the right.

Step 2:   Add the % symbol.

Example 1:
Convert 0.19 to a percent.

0.19 = 19   Move the decimal point two places to the right.

19 = 19%   Add the % symbol.

Example 2:
Convert 0.225 to a percent.

0.225 = 22.5   Move the decimal point two places to the right.

22.5 = 22.5%   Add the % symbol.

Example 3:
Convert 1.25 to a percent.

1.25 = 125   Move the decimal point two places to the right.

125 = 125%   Add the % symbol.

Convert the following decimals to percents.

1)	0.25	2)	0.50	3)	0.75	4)	1.0
5)	0.11	6)	0.17	7)	0.39	8)	0.86
9)	0.04	10)	0.12	11)	0.07	12)	0.115
13)	0.256	14)	0.333	15)	1.74	16)	0.185
17)	0.74	18)	0.1234	19)	1.21	20)	0.998

Hint:
Refer to the decimals chapter for more information about working with decimals.

CONVERTING PERCENTS TO FRACTIONS

Step 1:   Write the number over a denominator of 100 and drop the % symbol.

Step 2:   Express the fraction in lowest terms.

Example 1:

Convert 80% to a fraction.

$80\% = \frac{80}{100}$ Write the number over a denominator of 100 and drop the % symbol.

$\frac{80}{100} = \frac{8}{10} = \frac{4}{5}$ Express the fraction in lowest terms.

Example 2:

Convert 170% to a fraction.

$170\% = \frac{170}{100}$ Write the number over a denominator of 100 and drop the % symbol.

$\frac{170}{100} = 1\frac{70}{100} = 1\frac{7}{10}$ Express the fraction in lowest terms.

Hint:

Refer to the chapter on fractions for more information about working with fractions.

Remember:

Express fractions in lowest terms.

Convert the following percent to fractions, whole numbers or mixed numbers.

1) 75%   2) 25%   3) 50%   4) 60%

5) 39%   6) 45%   7) 119%   8) 125%

9) 300%   10) 800%   11) 1100%   12) 80%

13) 17.7%   14) 21.3%   15) 4.7%   16) 10.5%

CONVERTING FRACTIONS TO PERCENTS

Step 1:   Convert the fraction to a decimal by dividing the numerator by the denominator.

Step 2:   Move the decimal point two places to the right and add the % sign.

Example 1:

Convert $\frac{1}{4}$ to a percent.

$\frac{1}{4} = 0.25$ Convert the fraction to a decimal by dividing the numerator by the denominator.

$0.25 = 25\%$ Move the decimal point two places to the right and add the % sign.

Example 2:

Convert $1\frac{1}{4}$ to a percent.

$1\frac{1}{4} = 1.25$ Convert the fraction to a decimal by dividing the numerator by the denominator.

$1.25 = 125\%$ Move the decimal point two places to the right and add the % sign.

Convert the following fractions to percent.

1) $\frac{1}{4}$ 2) $\frac{1}{2}$ 3) $\frac{3}{4}$ 4) $\frac{1}{10}$

5) $\frac{1}{8}$ 6) $\frac{5}{8}$ 7) $\frac{7}{10}$ 8) $\frac{3}{16}$

9) $\frac{7}{8}$ 10) $\frac{7}{16}$ 11) $5\frac{4}{5}$ 12) $\frac{1}{16}$

13)   25   14) $9\frac{5}{16}$ 15) $\frac{3}{32}$ 16) $1\frac{1}{32}$

17) $\frac{11}{16}$ 18) $8\frac{3}{4}$ 19) $1\frac{1}{2}$ 20) $3\frac{9}{10}$

Complete the table below with the missing percent, decimal or fraction.

Percent	Decimal	Fraction
	0.0625	
		$\frac{1}{8}$
		$\frac{3}{16}$
25%		
31.25%		
	.375	
	.4375	
		$\frac{1}{2}$
		$\frac{9}{16}$
62.5%		
	.6875	
75%		
		$\frac{13}{16}$
		$\frac{7}{8}$
	.9375	
	1.00	

CALCULATING PERCENT

Percent describes a part of a whole. It compares two numbers: percent to the standard or base. You can calculate percent using either the percent formula or ratio/proportion. The examples demonstrate how to calculate percent using both methods. Try both methods and then decide which method you prefer.

- Percent formula:

$P = B \times R$

P = **Percentage** or part that is being compared with the base.
B = **Base** or the total amount.
R = **Rate** is the percent or a number over one hundred.

- Ratio/proportion:

$$\frac{percentage}{base} = \frac{rate}{100}$$

Hint:

Refer to the Ratio/ Proportion chapter for more information about working with ratios and proportions.

When you solve a problem using percent, you are calculating one of three things:

- the **Percentage** of a number
- the **Rate** or percent one number is of another
- the **Base** when the percent is known

Each of these is explained below.

CALCULATING THE PERCENTAGE OF A NUMBER

Step 1:   Write the formula.

Step 2:   Convert percents to decimals.

Step 3:   Substitute known values into the formula.

Multiply base (B) times rate (R).

Step 4:   Check your answer. Substitute the answer into the formula.
Cross multiply.

Answers on both sides of the equal sign should be the same.

Example 1:

Calculate 25% of 350.

Using the Percent Formula

$P = B \times R$	Write the formula.
$25\% = .25$	Convert percents to decimals.
$P = 350 \times .25$	Substitute known values into the formula. Multiply B times R.
$P = 87.5$	Twenty-five percent of 350 is 87.5.

Example 2:

Calculate 25% of 350.

Using Ratio/Proportion

$\dfrac{\text{percentage}}{\text{base}} = \dfrac{\text{rate}}{100}$	Set up the proportion.
$\dfrac{P}{350} = \dfrac{25}{100}$	Substitute known values into the proportion and cross multiply.
$100P = 350 \times 25$	
$100P = 8\,750$	
$P = \dfrac{8\,750}{100}$	
$P = 87.5$	Twenty-five percent of 350 is 87.5.

Hint:

Checking your Answer.
Step 1: Substitute your answer into the formula.
Step 2: Check your answer by cross multiplying to see that they are equal.

Calculate the following percents.

1) 10% of 100   2) 25% of 200   3) 45% of 75   4) 7% of 50

5) 45% of 25   6) 11% of 60   7) 75% of 350   8) 39% of 80

9) 115% of 65   10) 125% of 200   11) 110% of 100   12) 14% of 35

13) 10.5% of 80   14) 30% of 180   15) 22.5% of 360   16) 37.5% of 600

CALCULATING THE RATE

Sometimes you know the base and the percentage, but need to calculate the rate. You use the same basic formula but need to move the variables around a bit so you can solve for R.

Step 1: Write the formula.

Step 2: Substitute known values into the formula. Divide percentage (P) by base (B).

Step 3: Convert the decimal to a percent. Move the decimal 2 places to the right.

Hint:

Whatever you do on one side of the equal sign you have to do on the other.

Example 1:

15 is what percent of 75?

Using the Percent Formula

$P = B \times R$	Write the formula.
$15 = 75 \times R$	Substitute known values into the formula.
$\frac{15}{75} = R$	Divide P by B.
$0.2 = R$	
$0.2 = 20\%$	Convert the decimal to a percent. Move the decimal 2 places to the right.

Fifteen is 20% of 75.

Example 2:

15 is what percent of 75?

Using Ratio/Proportion

$\frac{\text{percentage}}{\text{base}} = \frac{\text{rate}}{100}$	Set up the proportion.
$\frac{15}{75} = \frac{R}{100}$	Substitute known values into the proportion and cross-multiply.
$15 \times 100 = 75R$	
$\frac{1\,500}{75} = R$	
$20\% = R$	Notice that answer is the percent.

Fifteen is 20% of 75.

PERCENT

Calculate the following rates. Round off to the nearest tenth.

1) 25 is what percent of 525?

2) 7 is what percent of 65?

3) 65 is what percent of 1 700?

4) 11 is what percent of 45?

5) 4 is what percent of 15?

6) 75 is what percent of 180?

7) 34 is what percent of 100?

8) 14 is what percent of 199?

9) 10 is what percent of 100?

10) 10 is what percent of 200?

11) 9 is what percent of 100?

12) 41 is what percent of 100?

13) 36 is what percent of 3 255?

14) 8 is what percent of 70?

15) 186 is what percent of 750?

16) 95 is what percent of 220?

CALCULATING THE BASE

Sometimes you know the rate and the percentage, but need to calculate the base. You use the same basic formula but need to move the variables around a bit so you can solve for base (B).

Step 1:   Write the formula.

Step 2:   Convert the percent to a decimal.

Step 3:   Substitute known values into the formula.
            Divide percent (P) by rate (R).

Example 1:

25% of what number is 8?

Using the Percent Formula

$P = B \times R$ Write the formula.

$25\% = 0.25$ Convert the percent to a decimal.

$8 = B \times 0.25$ Substitute known values into the formula. Divide P by R.

$\frac{8}{0.25} = B$

$32 = B$

Twenty-five percent of 32 is 8.

Example 2:

25% of what number is 8?

Using Ratio/Proportion

$\frac{percentage}{base} = \frac{rate}{100}$ Set up the proportion.

$\frac{8}{B} = \frac{25}{100}$ Substitute known values into the proportion and cross multiply.

$8 \times 100 = 25 \times B$

$\frac{800}{25} = B$

$32 = B$

Twenty-five percent of 32 is 8.

PERCENT

Calculate the following bases. Round answers to the nearest tenth.

1) 25% of what number is 30?

2) 10% of what number is 86?

3) 75% of what number is 5?

4) 14% of what number is 65?

5) 80% of what number is 45?

6) 12% of what number is 15?

7) 42% of what number is 21?

8) 15% of what number is 100?

9) 25% of what number is 4?

10) 12% of what number is 75?

11) 20% of what number is 100?

12) 10% of what number is 61.5?

13) 5% of what number is 14.7?

14) 75% of what number is 125?

15) 30% of what number is 21?

16) 7% of what number is 15.5?

CALCULATING INCREASES AND DECREASES USING PERCENT

CALCULATING AN INCREASE

Trade workers often estimate the amount of materials needed to complete a job. Estimating materials means adding on a percentage for waste, for example, concrete spillage and soil swell factors.

When you calculate an increase, you work with percentages that are greater than one hundred. For example, you may include 5% waste for the hardwood flooring required to complete a job. This means adding 5% onto the actual amount of hardwood flooring required.

Example 1:

The estimated concrete volume required for a concrete wall and footing is 30 cubic yards. An additional 10% of concrete is needed for spillage and priming the concrete pump.

Calculate the total cubic yards of concrete required.

One way to solve this type of problem is to calculate 10% of 30 cubic yards and then add the 10% to the original 30 cubic yards.

Another way is to think of the required concrete, 30 cubic yards, as equal to 100% plus 10% for spillage and priming the concrete pump for a total of 110%. Solving the problem this way allows you to calculate the total concrete required using one calculation.

Using Percent

$P = B \times R$ Write the formula.

$110\% = 1.10$ Add the percent waste to 100%.
Convert the percent to a decimal.

$P = 30 \times 1.10$ Substitute known values into the formula.
Multiply B times R.

$P = 33$

The total amount of concrete required is 33 cubic yards.

> **Example 2:**
>
> **Using Ratio/Proportion**
>
> $\dfrac{\text{percentage}}{\text{base}} = \dfrac{\text{rate}}{100}$ Set up the proportion.
>
> $\dfrac{P}{30} = \dfrac{110}{100}$ Substitute known values into the proportion and cross multiply.
>
> $100 \times P = 30 \times 110$
>
> $100P = 3\ 300$
>
> $P = \dfrac{3\ 300}{100}$
>
> $P = 33$
>
> The total amount of concrete required is 33 cubic yards.

Calculate the following.

1) A contractor estimated 45 cubic yards of concrete was required to pour a concrete wall and footing, plus 10% for spillage and priming the concrete pump. Calculate the total cubic yards of concrete required. Hint: Calculate the percentage (P).

2) It was estimated that 392 lineal feet of strip flooring was required to cover a 12' by 14' room. It actually took 439 lineal feet to cover the room. Calculate the percentage of waste. Hint: Calculate the rate (R).

3) A contractor invoiced an owner for $13,500 including 12.5% profit. Calculate the contractor's original costs before profit. Hint: Find the base(B).

CALCULATING A DECREASE

A decrease is the opposite of an increase. When you calculate a decrease, you work with percentages that are less than one hundred. This means the decrease is subtracted from the original amount. For example, a discounted tool or piece of equipment has been reduced from the original price, an apprentice's rate of pay is a percentage of the journeyperson's rate of pay, and the breaking strength of rope with a bend or knot in it is a percentage of the breaking strength of rope without bends or knots.

Example 1:

The breaking strength of $\frac{3}{4}$" nylon rope is 2 800 pounds under tension. If a knot is tied in the nylon rope the strength is reduced by 50%. Calculate the breaking strength of $\frac{3}{4}$" nylon rope with a knot tied in it.

Using the Percent Formula

$P = B \times R$ Write the formula.

$50\% = 0.50$ Subtract the percent from 100 and change to a decimal.

$P = .50 \times 2\ 800$ Substitute the known values into the formula. Multiply B times R.

$P = 1\ 400$ pounds

The breaking strength of $\frac{3}{4}$" nylon rope with a knot tied in it is 1 400 pounds.

Example 2:

Using Ratio/Proportion

$\dfrac{\text{percentage}}{\text{base}} = \dfrac{\text{rate}}{100}$ Set up the proportion.

$\dfrac{P}{2\ 800} = \dfrac{50}{100}$ Substitute known values into the proportion and cross multiply.

$P \times 100 = 50 \times 2\ 800$

$100P = 140\ 000$

$P = \dfrac{140\ 000}{100}$

$P = 1\ 400$ pounds

The breaking strength of $\frac{3}{4}$" nylon rope with a knot tied in it is 1 400 pounds.

Calculate the following decreases.

1) The breaking strength of $\frac{1}{2}''$ polyester rope is 1 200 pounds under tension. If a hitch is tied in the polyester rope the strength is reduced by 25%. Calculate the breaking strength of $\frac{1}{2}''$ polyester rope with a hitch tied in it.

2) The breaking strength of a $\frac{5}{8}''$ nylon rope is 2 000 pounds. Its strength is reduced by 10% when it is wet. What would the breaking strength of the nylon rope be when it is wet?

3) A table saw that retails for $215 is on sale at 20% off. What is the sale price of the saw?

PRACTICE

1) A contractor has to pay 7% PST plus 7% GST on $3 776 worth of building material.

   a) Calculate the total amount of tax paid on $3 776.

   b) Calculate the total paid including taxes.

2) A building had 35 cylindrical columns that needed to be poured. 60% of the columns were poured in the morning, and 40% were poured in the afternoon.

   a) How many columns were poured in the morning?

   b) How many columns were poured in the afternoon?

3) The total membership in a union is 3 208 members. 87.5% of the membership voted on the collective agreement. How many members voted?

   2807 members voted $3208 \times .875 = 2807$

4) A worker paid 21% income tax on his total earnings of $34 850. How much income tax did the worker pay?

5) A lumber supplier makes 16% profit on what is sold. If $2 845.50 of lumber is sold, what is the supplier's profit?

   $2845.50 \times .16 = 455.28$

6) Twenty of a total of 32 joists were installed before coffee break. What percent was installed?

7) A worker had $256.20 deducted from his paycheck. His gross (total before deductions) earnings were $1 220.00. Calculate the percent of deductions.

Hint:

You are calculating a decrease.

8) A lot takes up 43 560 square feet. The house and outbuildings occupy 6 534 square feet of the property. What percentage of the lot is taken up by the house and outbuildings?

9) A tool store offered a 15% discount to union carpenters. Calculate the discount price on the following tools:

    a) $254.80 saw

Hint:

You are calculating a decrease.

    b) $12.60 crow bar

    c) $38.40 level

10) Out of a total membership of 3 216 carpenters, 2 412 voted on a referendum.

    a) What percentage of the membership voted?

    b) What percentage did not vote?

11) The area of a floor is 125 square metres. There is a lumber allowance of 25% for waste and matching. How much flooring is needed?

12) The labour and material for renovating a building cost $4 375. Of this amount, 65% went for the cost of labour and the balance went for the cost of material.

    a)   What was the labour cost?

    b)   What was the material cost?

13) The labour and material for renovating a building cost $8 520. Seventy-eight percent of this amount was the cost for labour and the balance was the cost of material.

    a)   What was the labour cost?

    b)   What was the material cost?

14) It took a total of 8 545 hours to complete a job. Concrete formwork took 45% of the total hours. Calculate the number of hours spent on concrete formwork.

15) A double glazed window cost $585.00. The materials allowance to install the window is $4\frac{1}{2}\%$ of the cost. Calculate the total cost to the customer.

16)

The table, *Wage Scale as a Percentage of Employer's Journeyperson Wage.*, gives the percentage of a journeyperson's wage that an apprentice earns over a specific term. For example, an apprentice in the fifth month of apprenticeship would earn 50% of a journeyperson's wage. An apprentice in the first half of the third year of apprenticeship would earn 70% of a journeyperson's wage.

Calculate the hourly apprentice wage rates, based on a journeyperson rate of $25.40. The apprenticeship is a four-year term.

Wage Scale as a Percentage of Employer's Journeyperson Wage Period

Period (in months)	0-6	7-12	13-18	19-24	25-30	31-36	37-42	43-48	49-54	55-60
Five-year term	50%	55%	60%	65%	70%	75%	80%	80%	90%	90%
Four-year term	50%	55%	60%	65%	70%	75%	80%	90%		
Three-year term	50%	55%	65%	70%	80%	90%				
Two-year term	50%	60%	75%	90%						
One-year term	50%	90%								

a)   What percentage of the journeyperson rate would an apprentice in the 34th month of apprentice earn?

b)   How much does a carpentry apprentice in the 34th month of apprenticeship earn per hour?

c)   How much does a carpentry apprentice in the first half of the third year apprenticeship earn per hour?

d)   Calculate the hourly wage of a carpentry apprentice in the last half of the fourth year of apprenticeship.

PERCENT

INTRODUCTION

Ratio/Proportion is one of the most important mathematical applications you will use as a trades worker. You can use ratio/proportion to calculate increases and decreases, figure out percentages, compare rates and calculate rafter, gable stud and collar tie lengths.

When you have completed this chapter you will be able to:

- ❏ Write and simplify ratios.
- ❏ Write proportions and calculate the unknown quantity.
- ❏ Use proportion to solve similar triangles.
- ❏ Calculate direct proportions.
- ❏ Calculate indirect proportions.
- ❏ Compare two rates.
- ❏ Solve applications using ratio/proportion.

RATIOS

A ratio compares two numbers or quantities. For example, you can write a ratio to compare the amount of water to cement to make concrete. The two numbers in a ratio are called terms.

You can write ratios several ways:

$$1 \text{ to } 2 \qquad\qquad 1:2 \qquad\qquad \frac{1}{2}$$

For example, the ratio $\dfrac{1 \text{ water}}{2 \text{ cement}}$ would read 1 part water to two parts cement.

SIMPLIFYING RATIOS

Ratios should always be expressed in lowest terms.

> **Example 1:**
>
> $10 \text{ to } 30 = \frac{10}{30} = \frac{1}{3}$

Although ratios should be expressed in lowest terms, improper ratios are left as improper ratios.

> **Example 2:**
>
> $30 \text{ to } 10 = \frac{30}{10} = \frac{3}{1}$

Write whole number ratios as improper ratios.

> **Example 3:**
>
> $3 \text{ to } 1 = \frac{3}{1}$

Write the following ratios in their lowest terms.

1) 6/3   2) 5/20   3) 9/27   4) 36/4

5) 48:12   6) 15:3   7) 8:2   8) 10:5
    4:1   5:1   4:1   2:1

9) 27 to 9   10) 72 to 12   11) 10 to 150   12) 150 to 25
    3:1   6:1   1:15   6:1

PROPORTION

A proportion compares two ratios. Proportions are usually written as a pair of equivalent fractions.

Example 1:

$\frac{1}{2} = \frac{5}{10}$ 1:2 :: 5:10   1 is to 2 as 5 is to 10

Always read a proportion as two equal ratios connected by the word 'as'.

Example 2:

   1 is to 2 as 5 is to 10

The two cross products are equal in a proportion. Cross multiply to find the cross products.

Example 3:

$\frac{1}{2} \diagdown \frac{5}{10}$ $2 \times 5 = 1 \times 10$
                                                   $10 = 10$

There are two types of proportions: direct proportion and indirect proportion. The following table compares the difference between direct and indirect proportions:

Direct Proportion		Indirect Proportion	
$\frac{A}{B} = \frac{C}{D}$	$\frac{\text{increase}}{\text{decrease}} = \frac{\text{increase}}{\text{decrease}}$	$\frac{A}{B} = \frac{D}{C}$	$\frac{\text{increase}}{\text{decrease}} = \frac{\text{decrease}}{\text{increase}}$

Both direct proportion and indirect proportion are explained in this chapter.

DIRECT PROPORTION

A direct proportion compares two like quantities or two ratios that are directly proportional and equal to one another. This means an increase in one quantity leads to a proportional increase in the other quantity.

$$\frac{A}{B} = \frac{C}{D} \qquad\qquad \frac{increase}{decrease} = \frac{increase}{decrease}$$

Hint:

In a direct proportion, always make sure that whatever unit you place on the top in the first ratio is placed on the top in the second ratio.

SOLVING A DIRECT PROPORTION

Step 1: Set up a proportion.

Step 2: Substitute known values into the proportion and cross multiply.

Step 3: Divide to get the unknown value by itself.

Step 4: Check your answer by cross-multiplying.
The answer on both sides of the equal sign should be equal.

Example:

If one hammer costs \$32.00, what would the cost of ten hammers be?

$$\frac{A}{B} = \frac{C}{D}$$
Set up the proportion.

$$\frac{1 \text{ hammer}}{\$32.00} = \frac{10}{\chi}$$
Substitute known values into the proportion and cross-multiply.

$$\$32.00 \times 10 = 1 \times \chi$$

$$\frac{\$320.00}{1} = \chi$$
Divide to get the unknown value by itself.

$$\$320.00 = \chi$$

$$\$32.00 \times 10 = 1 \times \$320.00$$
Check your answer by cross-multiplying.

$$\$320.00 = \$320.00$$

Ten hammers will cost \$320.00.

Calculate the missing quantity in the following direct proportions.

1) $\dfrac{1}{2} = \dfrac{x}{8}$ **4**

2) $\dfrac{1}{3} = \dfrac{4}{x}$ **12**

3) $\dfrac{5}{x} = \dfrac{10}{16}$ **8**

4) $\dfrac{5}{15} = \dfrac{x}{60}$ **20**

5) $\dfrac{1}{5} = \dfrac{1.2}{x}$ **6**

6) $\dfrac{x}{75} = \dfrac{30}{25}$ **90**

7) $\dfrac{4}{7} = \dfrac{x}{56}$ **32**

8) $\dfrac{15}{10} = \dfrac{x}{150}$ **225**

9) $\dfrac{6}{x} = \dfrac{2}{3}$ **9**

10) $\dfrac{x}{20} = \dfrac{4}{5}$ **16**

11) $\dfrac{1.5}{25} = \dfrac{x}{1012}$ **60.72**

12) $\dfrac{5}{250} = \dfrac{25}{x}$ **1250**

13) $\dfrac{x}{42} = \dfrac{2}{3}$ **28**

14) $\dfrac{4}{9} = \dfrac{4.8}{x}$ **10.8**

15) $\dfrac{7}{9} = \dfrac{x}{36}$ **28**

16) $\dfrac{42}{3} = \dfrac{84}{x}$ **6**

SOLVING SIMILAR TRIANGLES

Triangles are similar if their matching angles are equal and the ratio of their corresponding sides is in proportion. Use proportion to calculate the length of the missing side in the similar triangles.

Step 1:   Draw a diagram and label it.

Step 2:   Set up a proportion with known values.

Step 3:   Cross-multiply.

Step 4:   Divide to get the x alone.

Step 5:   Check your answer. Cross-multiply. Answers on both sides of the equal sign should be equal.

Hint:
If the problem compares two things and you can locate three values, you can write and solve a proportion.

Example:

The two triangles below are similar triangles. Calculate the length of the unknown side using a proportion.

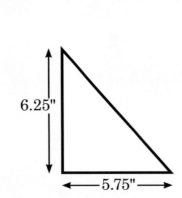

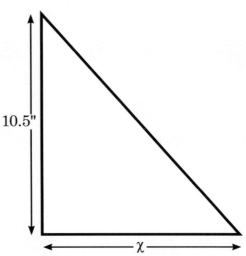

$$\frac{6.25}{5.75} = \frac{10.5}{\chi}$$ Set up a proportion.

$$6.25 \times \chi = 10.5 \times 5.75$$ Cross-multiply.

$$\chi = \frac{60.375}{6.25} = 9.66"$$ Divide to get the χ alone.

$$6.25 \times 9.66 = 10.5 \times 5.75$$ Check your answer.

$$60.375 = 60.375$$ Cross-multiply.

The answers should be equal.

Calculate the missing length. All measurements are in millimetres. Round off answers to two decimal places.

1)

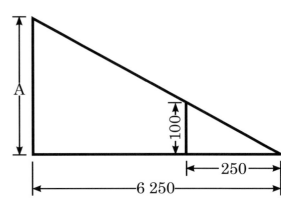

A =

2)

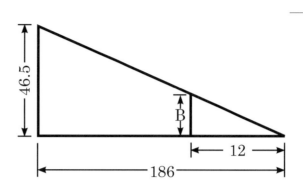

B =

3)

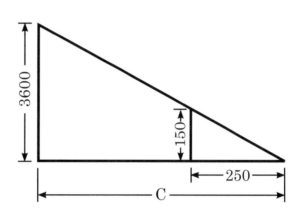

C =

4)

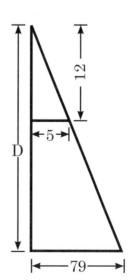

D =

5)

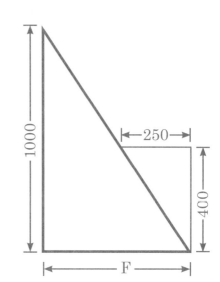

E =

6)

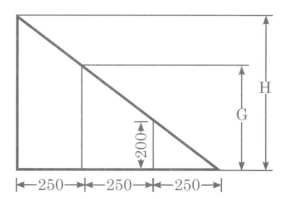

F =

7)

G =
H =

8)

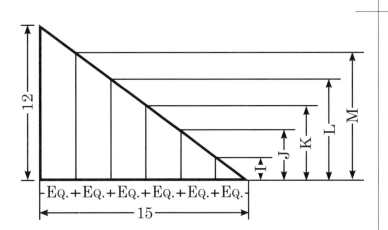

I =
J =
K =
L =
M =

9)

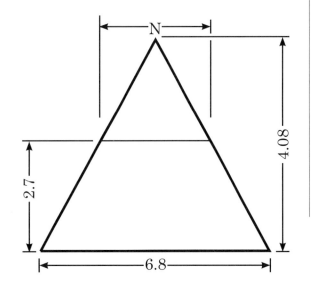

N =

10)

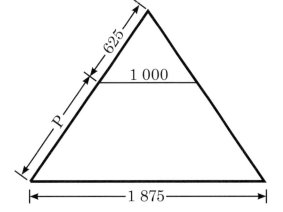

P =

11)

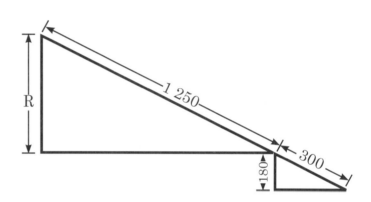

Q =

12)

R =

INDIRECT PROPORTION

An indirect proportion is a comparison between two quantities or ratios that are inversely proportional. This means an increase in one quantity leads to a decrease in the other quantity or when a decrease in one leads to an increase in the other. When you write an inverse proportion, either the first or the second ratio is inverted (flipped over).

$$\frac{A}{B} = \frac{D}{C} \qquad\qquad \frac{\text{increase}}{\text{decrease}} = \frac{\text{decrease}}{\text{increase}}$$

Solving a Indirect Proportion

You solve an indirect proportion the same way you solve a direct proportion. The only difference is in how you set up the proportion.

Step 1: Set up the proportion. Remember to invert either the first or second ratio.

Step 2: Substitute known values into the proportion and cross-multiply.

Step 3: Divide to get the unknown value by itself.

Step 4: Check your answer by cross-multiplying.
The answer on both sides of the equal sign should be equal.

Example 1:

If it takes 3 carpenters 30 days to build one house, how many days would it take for 5 carpenters to build the same house?

If the number of carpenters is increased from 3 to 5, the number of days to complete the house will be decreased.

$$\frac{A}{B} = \frac{D}{C}$$

Set up the proportion.
Remember to invert either the first or second ratio.

$$\frac{3 \text{ carpenters}}{5 \text{ carpenters}} = \frac{\chi \text{ days}}{30 \text{ days}}$$

Substitute known values into the proportion and cross-multiply.

$3 \times 30 = \chi \times 5$

$\dfrac{90}{5} = \chi$ Divide to get the unknown value by itself.

$18 = \chi$

$3 \times 30 = 18 \times 5$ Check your answer by cross-multiplying.

$90 = 90$

Example 2:

The diagram of the lever below was used to solve this indirect proportion. A lever is made up of a bar or rod that rests on a supporting point called a fulcrum. The fulcrum divides the lever into two parts called the effort arm and the resistance arm. Effort or force is applied to the effort arm which causes the resistance or load to move.

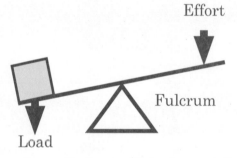

Effort

Fulcrum

Load

If a 200 pound force is applied to a 60 inch straight bar that is pivoted 4 inches from the end, what lift force is exerted? Hint: It is helpful to draw a diagram to solve a problem like this.

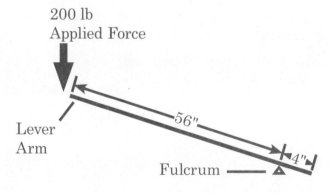

200 lb
Applied Force

Lever
Arm

56"

Fulcrum — 4"

$\dfrac{A}{B} = \dfrac{D}{C}$ Set up the proportion.
Remember to invert either the first or second ratio.

$$\frac{200 \text{ lbs applied force}}{\chi} = \frac{4 \text{ inch lever arm}}{56 \text{ inch lever arm}}$$

Substitute known values into the proportion and cross-multiply.

$200 \times 56 = \chi \times 4$

$\frac{11\ 200}{4} = \chi$

Divide to get the unknown value by itself.

$2\ 800 \text{ lbs} = \chi$

$200 \times 56 = 28\ 000 \times 4$

Check your answer by cross-multiplying.

$11\ 200 = 11\ 200$

The lift force is 2 800 lbs.

Calculate the missing value in the following indirect proportions.

1. If it takes 5 carpenters 80 days to build two houses, how many days would it take for 9 carpenters to build two houses?

2. If it takes 8 carpenters 26 days to complete a project, how many days would it take 11 carpenters to complete the same project?

3. If a 220 pound force is applied to a 64 inch straight bar that is pivoted 6 inches from the end, what lift force is exerted? Hint: It is helpful to draw a diagram to solve a problem like this.

4. If a 180 pound force is applied to a 60 inch straight bar that is pivoted 4.5 inches from the end, what lift force is exerted?

RATES

A rate is a ratio that compares two types of measurements. The denominator in a rate is usually 1. When you read a rate, you use the word 'per'.

Some common rates:

Kilometres per hour	100 km/hour means that in 1 hour you will travel 100 km
Millilitres per litre	Number of thousandths of a litre compared to one litre
Rpms per minute	Number of revolutions per minute.
Cost per unit	Cost per one unit

Using Rates to Compare

You can compare two rates when the same job is completed by two or more workers at different rates. The rate you are comparing is the length of time each worker takes. This type of comparison helps to estimate the costs of completing a job.

Step 1: Write a ratio for each worker. Divide the top by the bottom.

Step 2: Add the two answers.

Step 3: Set up the proportion.

Step 4: Substitute known values into the proportion and cross-multiply.

Step 5: Divide to get the unknown value by itself.

Step 6: Check your answer by cross-multiplying.
The answer on both sides of the equal sign should be equal.

Example:

A journeyperson takes 2 hours to install a door including trim and hardware. An apprentice takes 3.5 hours to do the same job. If they are working together to install one door, how long will it take?

Journeyperson
It takes a journeyperson 2 hours for 1 door.

Apprentice
It takes an apprentice 3.5 hours for 1 door.

Write a ratio for each worker. Divide the top by the bottom.

$$\frac{1}{2} = 0.5$$

$$\frac{1}{3.5} = 0.2857$$

$0.5 + 0.2857 = 0.7857$ hours

Add the two answers. Set up the proportion.

$$\frac{A}{B} = \frac{C}{D}$$

$$\frac{\chi}{1 \text{ door}} = \frac{60 \text{ minutes}}{0.7857 \text{ hours}}$$

Substitute the known values into the proportion and cross-multiply.

$\chi \times 0.7857 = 60 \times 1$

Divide to get the unknown value by itself.

$$\chi = \frac{60}{0.7857}$$

$\chi = 76.365$ minutes

Convert to hours and minutes. Sixty minutes equals one hour.

$76.365 \div 60 = 1.27275$ hours

Convert 0.27275 to minutes.
Multiply by 60.

$0.27275 \times 60 = 16.365$ minutes

It will take the journeyperson and the apprentice 1 hour and 16 minutes to install one door if they are working together.

Calculate the missing value in the following proportion.

1) A journeyperson takes 3 hours to install two doors including trim and hardware. An apprentice takes 6.75 hours to install two doors. If they are working together to install two doors, how long will it take?

PRACTICE

1) The concrete for a driveway is mixed at the ratio of 7 parts gravel to 2 parts cement. The foreman estimated 12 m³ gravel is needed. Calculate the amount of cement needed. Round your answer to the nearest tenth of m³.

$12 m^3 \div 7 = 1.714285714$

$1.714285714 \times 2 = 3.42$

$= 3.4 m^3$

2) The specified safety requirement for a sloped excavation is 0.75 horizontal to 1 vertical. Calculate the missing values in the table below.

	Horizontal	Vertical
a.	6'	
b.	8.5'	
c.		2 500 mm
d.		3 200 mm

3) If 3.6 kg of nails are used for each 90 m², how many kilos (kilograms) of nails are needed for 2 500 m²?

4) The lengths of the two rectangles shown below are proportional to their widths. Complete the table below.

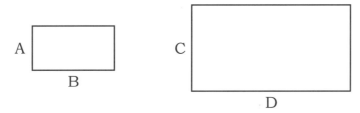

	A	B	C	D
a.		20 mm	54 mm	72 mm
b.	180 mm		480 mm	640 mm
c.	35 m	45 m		135 m
d.	22 m	38 m	48 m	

5) A proportion of 1:3:6 is used to mix cement, sand and gravel for concrete. How many cubic metres of each should be used to mix 86 m³ of concrete?

$86m^3 \div 10 = 8.6$
$C = 8.6 m^3$
$S = 25.8 m^3$
$G = 51.6 m^3$

Hint:
Indirect proportion.

6) If it takes 6 journeypersons 5 hours to complete a job, how long would it take 4 journeypersons to complete the same job?

7)   If it takes 8 carpenters to complete a formwork project in 5 days, how many carpenters would it take to complete the same project in four days?

$8.75 \div 5 = 1.75$

$3 \times 1.75 = 5.25 \, cm$

$4 \times 1.75 = 7 \, cm$

8)   The ratio of the sides of a triangle is 3:4:5. The longest side is 8.75 cm. Calculate the lengths of the two other sides.

INTRODUCTION

In this chapter you will learn to convert measurements using both the metric and the Imperial measuring systems. You will practice converting measurements within a measuring system, for example, inches to feet, cubic feet to cubic yards, and between measuring systems, for example, centimetres to inches.

As a trades worker you will use measurement to measure lengths, weights and volumes.

When you have completed this chapter you will be able to:

❏ Read Imperial tape measures to sixteenths of an inch.
❏ Read metric tape measures to millimetres.
❏ Convert between yards, feet and inches.
❏ Convert between metres, centimetres and millimetres.
❏ Convert between metric and Imperial units of measurement.
❏ Convert between squared units (area) of measurement.
❏ Convert between cubed units (volume) of measurement.

USING IMPERIAL AND METRIC

There are two measurement systems commonly used in the construction trades. They are the Imperial system and the International System of Units (SI), generally referred to as the metric system.

The Imperial system uses inches, feet, yards and miles for linear measurements. Weight is measured in pounds and ounces. Liquids are measured using pints and gallons. Imperial measurement is often used on job sites in the construction industry to order and measure building materials. For example, paint is ordered in gallons, pipe is ordered according to its diameter in inches, and loads are measured in pounds. Drawings on many job sites use feet and inches. Therefore, it is important to be able to use these units of measurement and to be able to convert between units of measurement within the Imperial System. For example, you need to be able to convert between inches, feet and yards.

The International System of Units (SI), or the metric system, is common in most countries including Canada. During technical training, you will primarily use the metric system. The metric system uses millimetres, centimetres, metres and kilometres for linear measurements. Weight is measured in grams, milligrams and kilograms. Liquids are measured using litres. Again, it is important to be comfortable using the metric system and to be able to convert between units of measurement within the metric system. For example, you need to be able to convert between millimetres and metres. Drawings that are in metric use millimetres for linear measurement but workers often convert millimetres to metres when measuring lengths.

THE IMPERIAL SYSTEM

Because the Imperial system is commonly used on job sites in the construction industry in Canada, trades workers must be comfortable working with measurements in fractions of an inch, inches and feet.

Rules for Writing Imperial Measurements

- Write abbreviations in lower case: in, yd, lb.
- The unit of measurement is always written in singular form.
- Leave a space between the amount and the unit of measurement: 4 in, 18 yd^3, 5 gal.

- The unit of measurement is written as an abbreviation when it follows a numeral: 4 in, 18 yd^3, 5 gal. When numbers are written as words, the unit of measurement is written in words: four inches, eighteen cubic yards, five gallons.

Note: In this math book, There are no periods after Imperial abbreviations.

Converting Within the Imperial System

Common Units of Measurement in the Imperial System		
Linear Measure	**Area Measure**	**Volume Measure for Solids**
12 in = 1 ft	144 in^2 = 1 ft^2	27 ft^3 = 1 yd^3
36 in = 1 yd	9 ft^2 = 1 yd^2	1 728 in^3 = 1 ft^3
3 ft = 1 yd	640 acres = 1 mi^2	**Volume Measure for Fluids**
1 760 yd = 1 mile	43 560 ft^2 = 1 acre	1 quart (qt) = 2 pints (pt)
5 280 ft = 1 mile		1 Imperial gallon (gal) = 4 qt
		Volume Measure Equivalents
		1 ft^3 = 6.24 Imperial gallons
		1 ft^3 = 7.5 US gallons

Symbols:		
inches: in, "	foot: ft, '	yard: yd
square inches: in^2 ⌗	square foot: ft^2 ⌗	square yard: yd^2
cubic inch : in^3	cubic foot: ft^3	cubic yard: yd^3
4 feet and 6 inches: 4' − 6", 4 ft 6 in		

Example 1:
  Convert 4 ft to inches.
  1 ft = 12 in

  4 ft = 4 × 12 = 48 in

Example 2:
  Convert 60 in to feet.
  1 ft = 12 in

  60 in = 60 ÷ 12 = 5 ft

> **Example 3:**
>   Convert 432 in^2 to square feet.
>
>   1 ft^2 = 144 in^2
>   432 in^2 = 432 in^2 ÷ 144 in^2 = 3 ft^2

> **Example 4:**
>   Convert 3 ft^3 to Imperial gallons.
>   1 ft^3 = 6.24 Imp gal
>   3 ft^3 = 3 ft^3 × 6.24 Imp gal = 18.72 Imp gal

Convert the following Imperial measurements to the units indicated.

1) 1' = _____ in

2) 2' = _____ in

3) 3' - 6" = _____ in

4) 7' - 9" = _____ in

5) 5' - 11" = _____ in

6) 56" = _____ ft _____ in

7) 126" = _____ ft _____ in

8) 221" = _____ ft _____ in

9) 1 yd = _____ ft = _____ in

10) 3 yd = _____ ft = _____ in

11) 6 yd = _____ ft = _____ in

12) 1 ft^2 = _____ in^2

13) 3 ft^2 = _____ in^2

14) 1 yd^2 = _____ ft^2 = _____ in^2

15) 4 yd^2 = _____ ft^2 = _____ in^2

16) 1 296 in^2 = _____ ft^2

17) 1 008 in^2 = _____ ft^2

18) 1 728 in^3 = _____ ft^3

19) 8 640 in^3 = _____ ft^3

20) 12 960 in^3 = _____ ft^3

21) 4 ft^3 = _____ in^3

22) 1 yd^3 = _____ ft^3

23) 270 ft^3 = _____ yd^3

24) 6 ft^3 = _____ Imperial gallons

25) 8.5 ft^3 = _____ Imperial gallons

26) 24 Imp gal = _____ ft^3

27) 46 Imp gal = _____ ft^3

28) 11 ft^3 = _____ US gallons

29) 3 ft^3 = _____ US gallons

30) 30 US gal   = _____ ft^3

Measuring Fractions

Trades workers constantly read and measure fractions when using the Imperial system. Errors in measurements are costly both in time and money. Experienced carpenters measure twice and cut once.

Trades workers work mostly in halves, fourths, eighths, sixteenths and occasionally in thirty-seconds depending on the degree of accuracy required.

Mark the measuring tape to show the following measurements.

1)   How many halves in one inch? _____

   a. $1\frac{1}{2}$ "   b. $3\frac{1}{2}$ "   c.   5"

2)   How many fourths in one inch? _____

   a. $\frac{1}{4}$ "   b. $2\frac{1}{4}$ "   c. $4\frac{3}{4}$

3) How many eighths in one inch? _____

a. $5\frac{3}{8}$ " b. $6\frac{5}{8}$ c. $7\frac{7}{8}$ "

4) How many sixteenths in one inch? _____

a. $\frac{3}{16}$ " b. $1\frac{7}{16}$ " c. $3\frac{15}{16}$ "

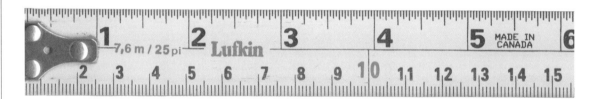

The illustrations below represent segments of an Imperial measuring tape. Write the measurements marked with arrows on the rulers.

Remember: count the lines not the spaces.

1)

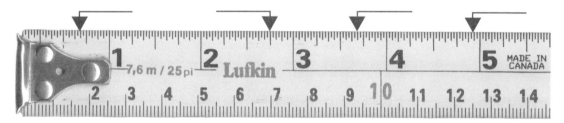

2)

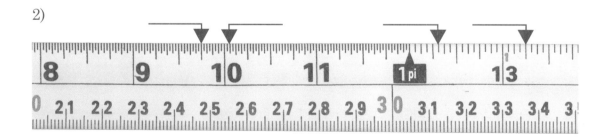

3)

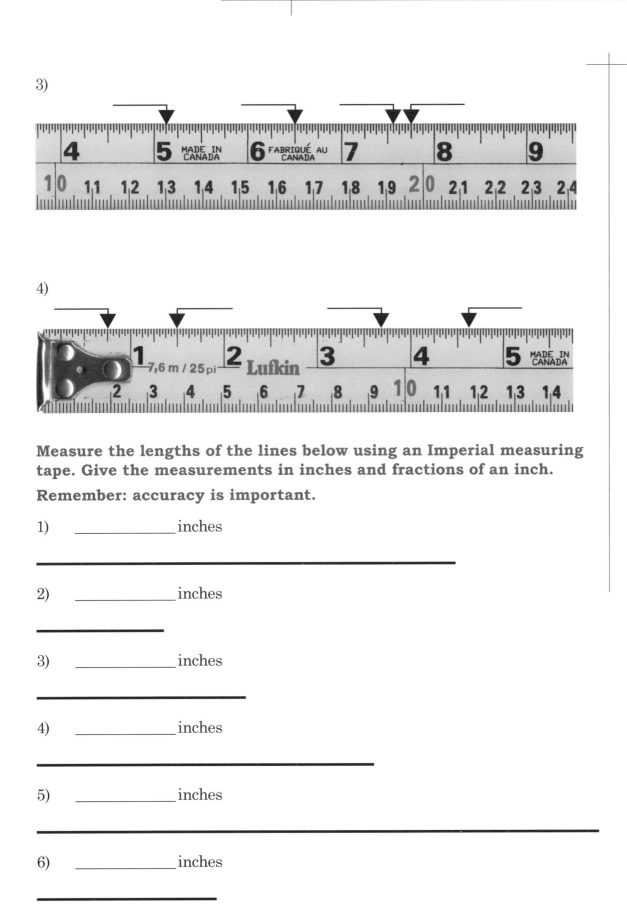

4)

Measure the lengths of the lines below using an Imperial measuring tape. Give the measurements in inches and fractions of an inch.

Remember: accuracy is important.

1) _____ inches

2) _____ inches

3) _____ inches

4) _____ inches

5) _____ inches

6) _____ inches

7) _____ inches

_____

8) _____ inches

_____

9) _____ inches

_____

10) _____ inches

_____

Adding and Subtracting Feet and Inches

Step 1: Line up the measurements.
Put like units under like units.

Step 2: Add or subtract the inches. Add or subtract the feet.

Step 3: Change the inches to feet (divide by 12).

Step 4: Rewrite the total.

Example 1:

5 ft 11 in		8 ft
+ 3 ft 9 in	20 in = 1 ft 8 in	+ 1 ft 8 in
8 ft 20 in		9 ft 8 in

Example 2:

8 ft 6 in
− 2 ft 6 in
6 ft 0 in

Example 3:

Sometimes you have to borrow one foot from the feet column.

$$
\begin{array}{rr}
6\text{ ft} & 2\text{ in} \\
-\ 2\text{ ft} & 8\text{ in} \\
\end{array}
$$
You can't subtract 8 in from 2 in. Borrow 1 ft.

$$
\begin{array}{rr}
5\text{ ft} & 14\text{ in} \\
-\ 2\text{ ft} & 8\text{ in} \\
\hline
3\text{ ft} & 6\text{ in} \\
\end{array}
$$
Subtract 1 ft from the feet column. Add 12 in to the inches column.

Example 4:

Sometimes there are fractions of an inch that need to be added or subtracted. You must follow the rules for adding and subtracting fractions.

$$
\begin{array}{rl}
5\text{ ft} & 6\frac{7}{8}\text{ in} \\
+\ 4\text{ ft} & 8\frac{3}{8}\text{ in} \\
\hline
9\text{ ft} & 14\frac{10}{8}\text{ in} = 9\text{ ft } 15\frac{2}{8}\text{ in} = 10\text{ ft } 3\frac{1}{4}\text{ in} \\
\end{array}
$$

Remember:

12 in. = 1 ft.

Example 5:

$$
\begin{array}{rl}
17\text{ft} & 5\frac{7}{8}\text{ in} \\
-\ 10\text{ft} & 2\frac{3}{4}\text{ in} \\
\hline
\end{array}
\quad = \quad
\begin{array}{rl}
17\text{ft} & 5\frac{7}{8}\text{ in} \\
-\ 10\text{ft} & 2\frac{6}{8}\text{ in} \\
\hline
7\text{ft} & 3\frac{1}{8}\text{ in} \\
\end{array}
$$

Hint:

Refer to the chapter on Fractions for more information about adding and subtracting fractions.

Add or subtract the following feet and inches.

1)
$$
\begin{array}{rr}
7\text{ ft} & 5\text{ in} \\
+\ 3\text{ ft} & 7\text{ in} \\
\hline
\end{array}
$$

2)
$$
\begin{array}{rr}
2\text{ ft} & 9\text{ in} \\
-\ & 11\text{ in} \\
\hline
\end{array}
$$

3)
$$
\begin{array}{rr}
5\text{ ft} & 6\text{ in} \\
-\ 3\text{ ft} & 5\text{ in} \\
\hline
\end{array}
$$

MEASUREMENT AND CONVERSION

4)
$$10 \text{ ft } 10 \text{ in}$$
$$+ \ 6 \text{ ft } \ 9 \text{ in}$$

5)
$$4 \text{ ft } \ 7 \text{ in}$$
$$+ \qquad 8 \text{ in}$$

6)
$$9 \text{ ft } \ 2 \text{ in}$$
$$- \ 4 \text{ ft } \ 7 \text{ in}$$

7)
$$9 \text{ ft } \qquad 9 \text{ in}$$
$$- \ 8 \text{ ft } \qquad 10 \text{ in}$$

8)
$$25 \text{ ft } \qquad 5 \text{ in}$$
$$+ \ 7 \text{ ft } \qquad 10 \text{ in}$$

9)
$$12 \text{ ft } \qquad 4 \text{ in}$$
$$- \ 5 \text{ ft } \qquad 11 \text{ in}$$

10)
$$2 \text{ ft } \quad 3\frac{1}{4} \text{ in}$$
$$+ \ 6 \text{ ft } \quad 4\frac{3}{4} \text{ in}$$

11)
$$4 \text{ ft } \quad 5\frac{3}{8} \text{ in}$$
$$+ \ 8 \text{ ft } \quad 3\frac{4}{8} \text{ in}$$

12)
$$24 \text{ ft } \quad 7\frac{5}{16} \text{ in}$$
$$+ \ 13 \text{ ft } \quad 4\frac{8}{16} \text{ in}$$

13)
$$5 \text{ ft } \quad 6\frac{5}{8} \text{ in}$$
$$+ \ 3 \text{ ft } \quad 8 \text{ in}$$

14)
$$7 \text{ ft } \quad 10\frac{3}{4} \text{ in}$$
$$+ \ 12 \text{ ft } \quad 9\frac{1}{2} \text{ in}$$

15)
$$27 \text{ ft } \quad 3\frac{3}{4} \text{ in}$$
$$+ \ 18 \text{ ft } \quad 10\frac{13}{16} \text{ in}$$

THE METRIC SYSTEM

The International System of Units (SI) is often referred to as the metric system within the construction industry. The International System of units sets the standards for the metric system and provides exact measurements that have the same meaning everywhere in the world.

The metric system is based on 10. Calculations with the metric system are done with numbers such as 10, 100 and 1 000. Converting units within the metric system means moving the decimal point a specific number of places to the right or to the left.

Prefixes in the metric system are the same for measuring length, volume and mass (weight), for example, kilometre, kilolitre and kilogram.

Rules for Writing Metric Measurements

- Write abbreviations in lower case: cm, mm, km. The one exception is litre. It is written as a capital L.

- The unit of measurement is always written in singular form. For example, cm and not cms.

- Periods are not used after unit abbreviations except when at the end of a sentence.

- There are no commas to indicate thousands, tens of millions and so on. Numbers are written with a space to separate: 10 000, 250 000.

- Leave a space between the amount and the unit of measurement: 25 cm.

- The unit of measurement is written as an abbreviation when it follows a numeral. For example, 4 cm, 13 m^3, 10 L. When numbers are written as words, the unit of measurement is written in words: four centimetres, thirteen cubic metres, ten litres.

Prefix Units	Symbol	Number of Base
tera	T	1 000 000 000 000
giga	G	1 000 000 000
mega	M	1 000 000
kilo	k	1 000
hecto	h	100
deca	da	10
No Prefix	Base Unit	1
deci	d	0.1
centi	c	0.01
milli	m	0.001
micro	µ	0.000 001
nano	n	0.000 000 001
pico	p	0.000 000 000 1

The highlighted rows are commonly used in the construction industry.

Common Units of Measurement in the Metric System

Linear Measure	Area Measure	Volume Measure for Solids
10 mm = 1 cm	100 mm^2 = 1 cm^2	1 m^3 = 1 000 000 cm^3
1 000 mm = 1 m	1 000 000 mm^2 = 1 m^2	**Volume Measure for Fluids**
100 cm = 1 m		1 L = 1 000 mL
		Volume Measure Equivalents
		1 kg = 1 000 000 mg

Letter Symbols:

millimetre: mm   millimetre squared: mm^2 cubic millimetre: mm^3

centimetre: cm   centimetre squared: cm^2 cubic centimetre: cm

metre: m   metre squared: m^2 cubic metre: m^3

litre: L   millilitre: mL   kilogram: kg   milligrams: mg

Converting Units

The table below is used to demonstrate a quick method of converting from one unit to another within the metric system. When you convert from one unit to another, the way the measurement is expressed changes. In other words, the number and the prefix change, but the length, volume or weight of the object does not change.

thousands	hundreds	tens	Base Units	tenths	hundredths	thousandths
kilometre	hectometre	decametre	metre	decimetre	centimetre	millimetre
km	hm	dam	m	dm	cm	mm
kilolitre	hectolitre	decalitre	litre	decilitre	centilitre	millilitre
kL	hL	daL	L	dL	cL	mL
kilogram	hectogram	decagram	gram	decigram	centigram	milligram
kg	hg	dag	g	dg	cg	mg

The highlighted boxes or cells are commonly used by workers in the construction trades

---

Example 1:

A brick wall measures 450 000 mm in length.
Convert 450 000 mm to metres.

You are moving from small units to large units.

Step 1: Place a decimal after the amount. **450 000.**

Step 2: Locate the prefix of the known amount on the table. **milli**

Step 3: Locate the prefix or the base unit that you are converting to. **metre**

Step 4: Move the decimal point the same number of places in the same direction you move on the table. **450.000 m**

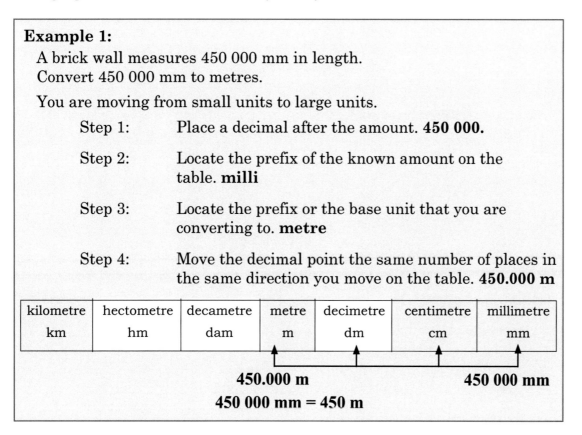

kilometre	hectometre	decametre	metre	decimetre	centimetre	millimetre
km	hm	dam	m	dm	cm	mm

450.000 m   450 000 mm

450 000 mm = 450 m

Note:

This set of steps only works for linear measures.

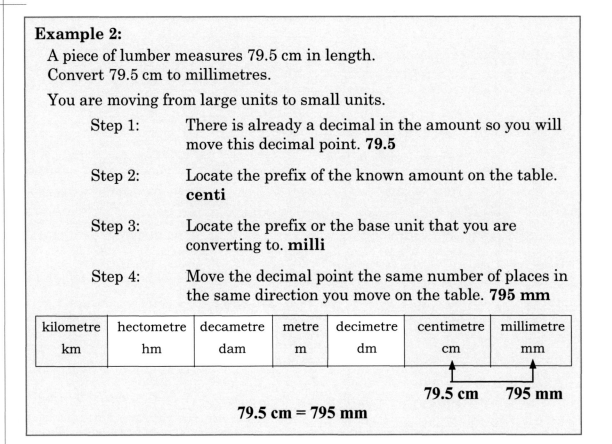

Example 2:

A piece of lumber measures 79.5 cm in length.
Convert 79.5 cm to millimetres.

You are moving from large units to small units.

Step 1:　　There is already a decimal in the amount so you will move this decimal point. **79.5**

Step 2:　　Locate the prefix of the known amount on the table. **centi**

Step 3:　　Locate the prefix or the base unit that you are converting to. **milli**

Step 4:　　Move the decimal point the same number of places in the same direction you move on the table. **795 mm**

kilometre	hectometre	decametre	metre	decimetre	centimetre	millimetre
km	hm	dam	m	dm	cm	mm

79.5 cm = 795 mm

Convert the following units.

1)　1 cm　　　　= _____ mm

2)　1 m　　　　= _____ mm

3)　1 m　　　　= _____ cm

4)　8 m　　　　= _____ mm

5)　35 mm　　　= _____ cm

6)　155 mm　　 = _____ cm

7)　100 mm^2　= _____ cm^2

8)　900 mm^2　= _____ cm^2

9)　375 mm^2　= _____ cm^2

10)　6 cm^2　　= _____ mm^2

11)　17 cm^2　= _____ mm^2

12) $1\ 000\ 000\ mm^2$ = _____ m^2

13) $5\ 000\ 000\ mm^2$ = _____ m^2

14) $9\ 500\ 000\ mm^2$ = _____ m^2

15) $1\ 000\ mL$ = _____ L

16) $11\ 000\ mL$ = _____ L

17) $4\ 500\ mL$ = _____ L

18) $10\ L$ = _____ mL

19) $22\ L$ = _____ mL

20) $1.4\ L$ = _____ mL

21) $3.2\ L$ = _____ mL

22) $1\ kg$ = _____ mg

23) $6\ kg$ = _____ mg

24) $2.7\ kg$ = _____ mg

25) $1\ m^3$ = _____ cm^3

26) $4\ m^3$ = _____ cm^3

27) $6.4\ m^3$ = _____ cm^3

28) $1\ 000\ 000\ cm^3$ = _____ m^3

29) $8\ 000\ 000\ cm^3$ = _____ m^3

30) $2\ 500\ 000\ cm^3$ = _____ m^3

Measuring Centimetres and Millimetres

Trades workers read and measure centimetres and millimetres when using the metric system. You will use the metric system during technical training and on some jobs. Millimetres are commonly used for measurements on blueprints but can be awkward to calculate lengths, areas and volumes because of the number of digits. It is often more convenient to convert millimetres to metres to make calculations and to measure lengths.

MEASUREMENT AND CONVERSION

> **Example:**
>   Calculate the area of wall that measures 12 000 mm by 3 000 mm.
>
>   In millimetres
>   Area = L × W
>   = 12 000 mm × 3 000 mm
>   = 36 000 000 mm²
>
>   In metres
>   Area = L × W
>   = 12 m × 3 m
>   = 36 m²
>
>   It would be very easy to miss one of the zeros or to add one zero too many when working in mm. Converting millimetres to metres makes the calculation less awkward.

Draw an arrow to show the following measurements.

1) a. 9 mm   b. 30 mm   c. 85 mm

2) a. 16 cm   b. 23 cm   c. 29 cm

3) a. 12 mm   b. 12 cm   c. 14.5 cm

4) a. 25 mm   b. 7.7 cm   c. 112 mm

The illustrations below represent segments of a metric measuring tape. Write the measurements marked with arrows on the tapes.

Remember: Count the lines not the spaces.

1)

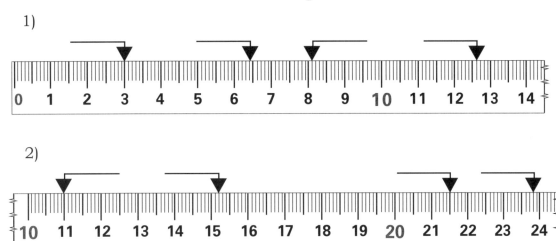

2)

3)

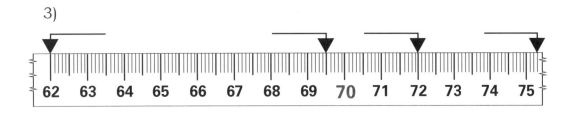

4)

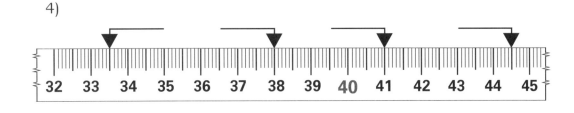

5)

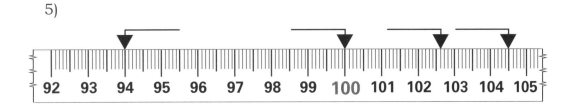

MEASUREMENT AND CONVERSION

Use a metric measuring tape to measure the lines below.

1) ———————————————

    mm _____   cm _____   m _____

2) ———————————————————

    mm _____   cm _____   m _____

3) ————————

    mm _____   cm _____   m _____

4) ———————————————

    mm _____   cm _____   m _____

5) —————————

    mm _____   cm _____   m _____

6) ——————————————

    mm _____   cm _____   m _____

7) —————————————————

    mm _____   cm _____   m _____

8) —————————————

    mm _____   cm _____   m _____

9) ———————————————————————

    mm _____   cm _____   m _____

10) ———————————————

    mm_____   cm _____   m _____

CONVERTING BETWEEN METRIC AND IMPERIAL

Some common conversions are:

1" = 2.54 cm

39" = 1 m

$1.3 \text{ yd}^3 = 1 \text{ m}^3$

2.2 lb = 1 kg

Example 1:
Convert 6" to centimetres.
1" = 2.54 cm
6" = 6" × 2.54 = 15.24 cm

Example 2:
Convert 25 cm to inches.
1" = 2.54 cm
25 cm = 25 cm ÷ 2.54 = 9.8"

Example 3:
Convert 10" to millimetres.
1" = 2.54 cm
10" = 10" × 2.54 = 25.4 cm
25.4 cm = 254 mm

Example 4:
Convert 655 mm to inches.
655 mm = 65.5 cm
65.5 cm = 65.5 cm ÷ 2.54 = 25.8"

MEASUREMENT AND CONVERSION

Convert the following measurements. Round off to two decimal places.

1) a) 1" =_____ cm   b) 7" =_____cm   c) 15" = ____ mm

2) a) 5 cm =_____"   b) 75 cm =_____"   c) 105 cm = _____"

3) a) 39" =_____ m   b) 84" =_____m   c) 3' = _____ m

4) a) 6 m =_____"   b) 2.5 m =_____"   c) 8 m = _____ ft

5) a) 1.3 yd^3 =_____ m^3 b) 5 yd^3 =_____ m^3 c) 7.9 yd^3 = ____ m^3

6) a) 3 m^3 =_____yd^3 b) 9.2 m^3 =____ yd^3 c) 5 m^3 =____yd^3

7) a) 1 kg =_____ lb   b) 12 kg =_____lb   c) 15.6 kg = _____ lb

8) a) 25 lb =_____kg   b) 64 lb =_____ kg   c) 128 lb =_____kg

INTRODUCTION

PERIMETER, AREA AND VOLUME

This section of the math book begins with an introduction to formulas and how to use them, and a table with formulas for perimeter, area and volume. Not all of the formulas in the table are covered in this math book. They have been included because you will encounter them during your technical training as an apprentice. Perimeter, area, volume and right-angle triangles are each covered separately in the following four chapters.

It is important that you understand the difference between perimeter, area and volume, and how each is measured. The table below compares perimeter, area and volume.

12" = 1'	144 in^2 = 1 ft^2	1,728 in^3 = 1 ft^3
↓	↓	↓
perimeter	area	volume
One-dimensional	Two-dimensional	Three-dimensional
inches	in^2	in^3
feet	ft^2	ft^3
yards	yd^2	yd^3
mm	mm^2	mm^3
cm	cm^2	cm^3
m	m^2	m^3

Using Formulas

Formulas and equations use mathematical abbreviations, symbols and constants. You need to know these abbreviations and symbols to solve formulas. You need to know how to move numbers, letters and symbols across the equal sign.

Formula: a mathematical rule expressed in symbols

Equation: a statement that two mathematical expressions are equal

Variable or unknown: letter or symbol used to represent a number

There are rules you must follow when you use a formula or solve an equation. The rules stay the same. Sometimes workers in the construction trades remember a short cut but the rules for solving the equation do not change.

Rules Used in Formulas

❒ Letters and symbols are used to represent numbers or quantities.

P	=	perimeter
A	=	area
V	=	volume
C	=	circumference
L	=	length
W	=	width
s	=	side
d	=	diameter
r	=	radius
b	=	base
h or H	=	height
π	=	pi (pronounced 'pie')

Examples:

A = LW means area equals length times width

$V = \pi r^2 h$ means volume equals pi times radius squared times height

❏ BEDMAS

Always follow the order of operations when solving an equation.

	Symbol
Brackets	( )
Exponents	3^2 $3^2 = 3 \times 3$ 3^3 $3^3 = 3 \times 3 \times 3$
Division	÷
Multiplication	×
Addition	+
Subtraction	−

Any operation performed on one side of the equal sign must be performed on the other side of the equal sign. Inverse operations are used to solve formulas and equations. Inverse means opposite. An inverse operation undoes an operation.

Addition equations are solved using subtraction.

$$\chi + 4 = 7$$
$$\chi + 4 - 4 = 7 - 4$$
$$\chi = 3$$

Subtraction equations are solved using addition.

$$\chi - 4 = 7$$
$$\chi - 4 + 4 = 7 + 4$$
$$\chi = 11$$

Multiplication equations are solved using division.

$$\chi \times 3 = 15$$
$$\frac{\chi \times 3}{3} = \frac{15}{3}$$
$$\chi = 5$$

Division equations are solved using multiplication.

$$\frac{\chi}{4} = 6$$
$$\frac{\chi}{4} \times 4 = 6 \times 4$$
$$\chi = 24$$

- ♦ Height or Altitude

  The perpendicular distance between the base and the opposite side is the height (h) or altitude (a). Some math books use altitude, others use height. This math book uses height (h) in formulas for perimeter, area and volume.

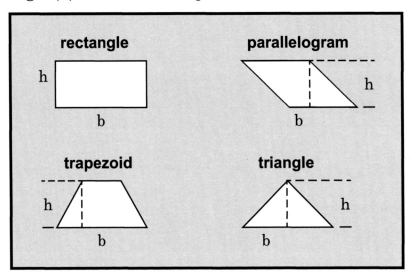

- ♦ Units of Measurement

  Always include the units of measurement. This is especially important when you are calculating perimeter, area and volume.

			Metric	Imperial
perimeter	linear measurement one-dimensional	mm cm m	in ft yd
area	squared units two-dimensional	mm^2 cm^2 m^2	in^2 ft^2 yd^2
volume	cubed units three-dimensional	mm^3 cm^3 m^3	in^3 ft^3 yd^3

- ♦ Pi (pronounced 'pie')

  Pi is used to calculate the circumference, area and volume of circles. The symbol 'π' is the ratio of the circumference of a circle to its diameter. Pi, a Greek letter that means perimeter, is always the same number, 3.14, no matter how large or small the circle is. Pi is an infinite decimal which means the decimal never ends. Computers have calculated pi to over 50 000 decimal places. Pi is an irrational number meaning it cannot be written as a fraction and has no repeating pattern.

For simplicity in everyday calculations, the approximation 3.14 or 3.1416 is used depending on the level of accuracy required. Pi can also be written as 22/7.

♦ Multiplication or Division

Both multiplication and division can be shown several ways.

Multiplication:

$3 \times 4 = 3 \cdot 4 = (3)(4) =$

Division:

$3 \div 4 = \dfrac{3}{4} \quad 4\overline{)3}$

♦ Exponents and Square Roots

Exponents:

$$\text{base} \longrightarrow 2^2 \longleftarrow \text{exponent}$$

$2^2 = 2 \times 2 = 4$

$2^3 = 2 \times 2 \times 2 = 8$

Square roots are represented by the symbol '$\sqrt{}$'. Taking the square root of a number is the opposite of squaring it.

Perfect Square	$\sqrt{}$
$\sqrt{1}$	1
$\sqrt{4}$	2
$\sqrt{9}$	3
$\sqrt{16}$	4
$\sqrt{25}$	5
$\sqrt{36}$	6
$\sqrt{49}$	7
$\sqrt{64}$	8
$\sqrt{81}$	9
$\sqrt{100}$	10

Perfect Square	$\sqrt{}$
$\sqrt{121}$	11
$\sqrt{144}$	12
$\sqrt{169}$	13
$\sqrt{196}$	14
$\sqrt{225}$	15
$\sqrt{256}$	16
$\sqrt{289}$	17
$\sqrt{324}$	18
$\sqrt{361}$	19
$\sqrt{400}$	20

BASIC GEOMETRIC SHAPES

The basic geometric shapes are square, rectangle, triangle, parallelogram, trapezoid, hexagon and circle.

- ◆ Square

  A square has four equal sides that are perpendicular or at "right angles" to each other. The sum of the four angles in a square is always equal to 360°.

$P = s + s + s + s = 4s$

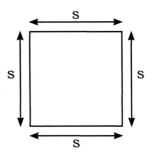

$A = LW \text{ or } A = s^2$

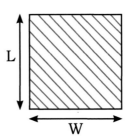

$V = LWH \text{ or } A = s^3$

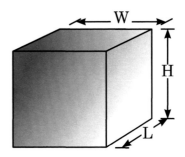

♦ Rectangle

A rectangle has 4 sides. The opposite sides are equal and the sides are perpendicular to each other. The sum of the four angles in a rectangle is always equal to 360°.

$P = 2(L+W)$

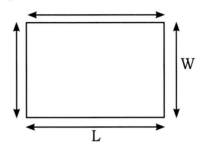

$A = LW$

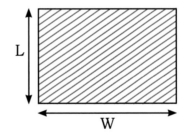

$V = LWH$

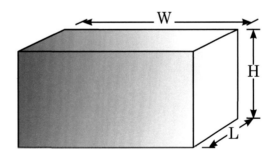

♦ Triangle

A triangle has 3 sides and 3 angles. The sum of the angles is always equal to 180°.

$P = s^1 + s^2 + s^3$

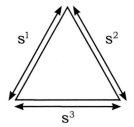

$A = \dfrac{1}{2}\, bh = \dfrac{bh}{2}$

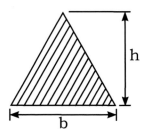

The three-dimensional figure of a triangle is called a triangular prism.

$V = $ area of base × h

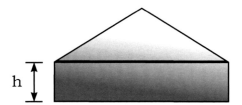

♦ Parallelogram

A parallelogram is a 4-sided figure. The opposite sides are parallel and equal in length. The sum of the four angles in a parallelogram is 360°.

$P = 2(s_1 + s_2)$

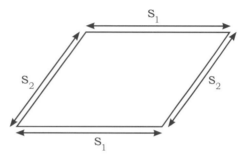

$A = bh$

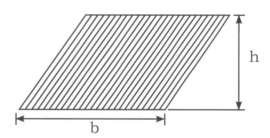

V = area of base × h

♦ Trapezoid

A trapezoid is a 4-sided figure that has two parallel sides. The two parallel sides are called bases. The height is a perpendicular line dropped from the shorter base to the longer base. The sum of the four angles in a trapezoid is 360°.

$$P = s_1 + s_2 + s_3 + s_4$$

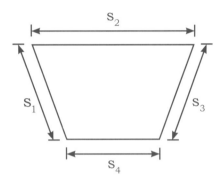

$$A = \left(\frac{b_1 + b_2}{2}\right) h$$

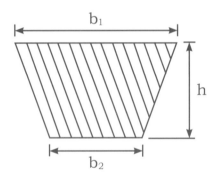

$$V = \text{area of base} \times h$$

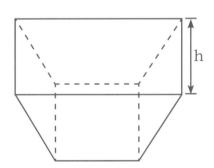

♦ Hexagon

A hexagon is a 6-sided figure. The 6 sides are equal in length.

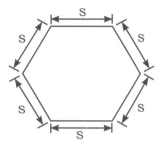

P = 6s

A = 2.59 × s^2

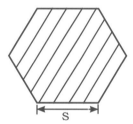

V = area of base × h

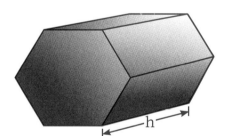

♦ Circle

A circle is a closed curved line. The distance to the centre point is the same at any point along the circle.

A straight line drawn from the centre of a circle to the edge is called the radius.

A straight line drawn through the centre of a circle, from one edge to the other, is called the diameter. The diameter equals twice the length of the radius.

The distance around the outside of a circle is called the circumference.

$C = \pi d$ or $2\pi r$

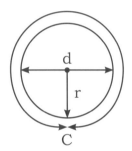

$A = \pi r^2$

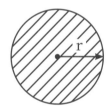

$V = \dfrac{4\pi r^3}{3}$ or $\dfrac{\pi d^3}{6}$

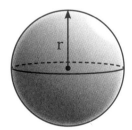

FORMULAS FOR PERIMETER, AREA AND VOLUME

Perimeter 1 - Dimensional	Area 2 - Dimensional	Volume 3 - Dimensional
$P = 2(L + W)$	$A = LW$	$V = LWH$
$P = 4s$	$A = s^2$	$V = s^3$
$P = s_1 + s_2 + s_3$	$A = \dfrac{bh}{2}$	$V = \text{area of base} \times h$
$\text{diameter} = 2 \times \text{radius}$ $\text{radius} = \dfrac{\text{diameter}}{2}$ $C = \pi d$ or $C = 2\pi r$	$\text{L.A.} = \pi dh$ $\text{S.A.} = \text{L.A.} + \text{area of both bases}$ $A = \pi r^2$	$V = \pi r^2 h$ $V = \dfrac{\pi r^2 h}{3}$ $V = \dfrac{\pi d^3}{6}$ or $V = \dfrac{4\pi r^3}{3}$

INTRODUCTION TO GEOMETRY

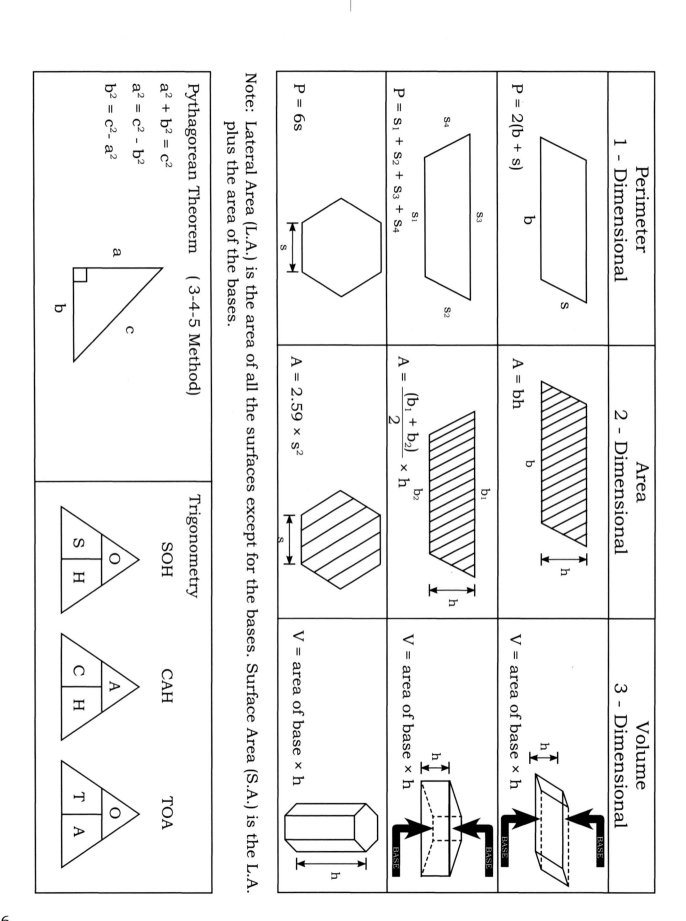

Perimeter 1 - Dimensional	Area 2 - Dimensional	Volume 3 - Dimensional
$P = 2(b + s)$	$A = bh$	V = area of base × h
$P = s_1 + s_2 + s_3 + s_4$	$A = \dfrac{(b_1 + b_2)}{2} \times h$	V = area of base × h
$P = 6s$	$A = 2.59 \times s^2$	V = area of base × h

Note: Lateral Area (L.A.) is the area of all the surfaces except for the bases. Surface Area (S.A.) is the L.A. plus the area of the bases.

Pythagorean Theorem   (3-4-5 Method)

$a^2 + b^2 = c^2$

$a^2 = c^2 - b^2$

$b^2 = c^2 - a^2$

Trigonometry

SOH   CAH   TOA

PERIMETER

INTRODUCTION

Perimeter is one-dimensional. It is a length or linear measurement that you can measure with a measuring tape. The perimeter of any figure, for example, rectangle, triangle or circle, is the distance around it.

12" = 1'	144 in² = 1 ft²	1,728 in³ = 1 ft³
↓	↓	↓
perimeter	area	volume
One-dimensional	Two-dimensional	Three-dimensional
inches	in²	in³
feet	ft²	ft³
yards	yd²	yd³
mm	mm²	mm³
cm	cm²	cm³
m	m²	m³

When you have completed this chapter you will be able to:

❐ Calculate the perimeter of rectangles, squares, triangles, circles, parallelograms, trapezoids and hexagons using formulas.

❐ Calculate the perimeter of complex shapes using a combination of formulas.

❐ Solve word problems using perimeter.

❐ Solve applications using perimeter.

CALCULATING PERIMETER

Always use the same steps to calculate perimeter.

Step 1:   Draw a diagram and label it.

Remember: All measurements must be in the same unit of measurement before you calculate perimeter. Refer to the Measurements and Conversions chapter for help converting units.

Step 2:   Write the formula.

Step 3:   Calculate the perimeter.

Example 1:

Calculate the perimeter of the rectangle below.

Step 1:   Draw a diagram and label it.

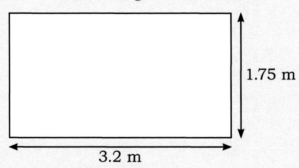

Step 2:   Write the formula.
P = 2(L + W)

Step 3:   Calculate the perimeter.
P = 2(3.2 m + 1.75 m) = 2(4.95 m) = 9.9 m

The perimeter is 9.9 m.

Example 2:

Calculate the circumference of the circle below.

      Step 1:   Draw a diagram and label it.

      Step 2:   Write the formula.
                      $C = \pi d$

   Note: If your calculator does not have π, use 3.1416. Your answer will be slightly different because it is slightly less accurate.

      Step 3:   Calculate the circumference.
                      $C = \pi d = \pi \times 2 \text{ ft} = 6.28 \text{ ft}$

                      The circumference is 6.28 ft.

Example 3:

Calculate the perimeter of the trapezoid below.

      Step 1:   Draw a diagram and label it.

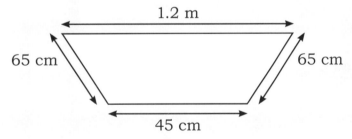

   Note: One of the measurements is in metres. Convert metres to centimetres. 1.2 m = 120 cm

      Step 2:   Write the formula.
                      $P = s^1 + s^2 + s^3 + s^4$

      Step 3:   Calculate the perimeter.
                      $P = s^1 + s^2 + s^3 + s^4 = 65 \text{ cm} + 120 \text{ cm} + 65 \text{ cm} + 45 \text{ cm} = 295 \text{ cm}$

                      The perimeter is 295 centimetres.

Calculate the perimeter of the following figures.

1)   P =
      Length = 47.8 cm
      Width = 39.3 cm

Remember:

The bases are parallel.

2)   P =
      Length = 18 in
      Width = 2 ft - 4 in

3)   C =
      Diameter = 29 mm

4)   C =
      Radius = 15 cm

5)   C =
      Diameter = 9 in

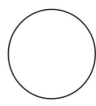

6)   C =
      Radius = 2.4 ft

7)   P =
      Sides = 125 cm
      Big base = 2 m
      Small base = 1.2 m

8) P =
   Sides = 2 ft
   Big base = 5 ft
   Small base = 18 in

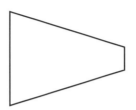

9) P =
   Side 1 = 25 cm
   Side 2 = 45 cm
   Side 3 = 25 cm

10) P =
    Side 1 = 3 ft
    Side 2 = 12 in
    Side 3 = 3.5 ft

11) P =
    Side 1 and 3 = 1.2 m
    Side 2 and 4 = 55 cm

12) P =
    Side 1 and 3 = 15 in
    Side 2 and 4 = 29 in

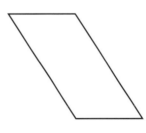

13) P =
    Side = 15 mm

14) P =
    Side = 3.1 ft

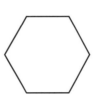

CALCULATING A SIDE WHEN YOU KNOW THE PERIMETER

If you know the perimeter and one of the sides you can calculate the missing side. Use the same formula you would if you were calculating the perimeter.

Example 1:

Calculate the diameter of a circle with a circumference of 25 cm. Round off your answer to two decimal places.

Step 1: Draw a diagram and label it.

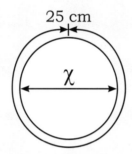

25 cm

χ

Step 2: Write the formula.
$C = \pi d$

Step 3: Calculate the diameter.
$25 \text{ cm} = \pi d$

$$\frac{25}{\pi} = d$$

$7.96 = d$

The diameter of the circle is 7.96 cm.

Example 2:

Calculate the length of a rectangle that has a perimeter of 84 ft and a width of 16 ft.

Step 1: Draw a diagram and label it.

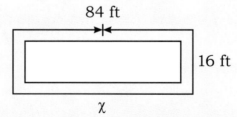

84 ft

16 ft

χ

Step 2: Write the formula.
$P = 2(L + W)$

Step 3:   Calculate the length.

$$84 = 2(\chi + 16)$$

$$\frac{84}{2} = \chi + 16$$

$$42 = \chi + 16$$
$$42 - 16 = \chi$$
$$26 = \chi$$

The length of the rectangle is 26 feet.

Calculate the missing side or diameter of the following figures. Round answers off to two decimal places.

1)   Calculate the diameter of a circle with a circumference of 3.2 ft.

2)   Calculate the diameter of a circle with a circumference of 15.8 m.

Hint:

3)   Calculate the radius of a circle with a circumference of 39 in.

The radius is equal to half of the diameter.

4) Calculate the length of a rectangle that has a perimeter of 112 ft and a width of 12.5 ft.

5) Calculate the width of a rectangle that has a perimeter of 865 mm and a length of 310 mm.

6) Calculate the width of a rectangle that has a perimeter of 4 ft – 6 in and a length 1 ft – 9 in.

CALCULATING THE PERIMETER OF COMPLEX SHAPES

Sometimes you need to do several calculations to get the final answer. Many perimeter problems are a combination of common geometrical shapes. To solve these problems, you will need to divide the figure into shapes you are familiar with and calculate the perimeter of each of those shapes. You might need to use the same formula several times or you might need to use several different formulas.

Example 1:

Calculate the perimeter of the deck below.

Step 1:   Draw a diagram and label it.

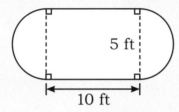

Step 2:   Write the formula(s).

The two half-circles make one complete circle. You need to calculate the circumference of the circle and add the two lengths of the rectangle. The two widths of the rectangle are not part of the perimeter.

$$C = \pi d$$

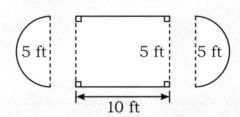

Step 3:   Calculate the perimeter.
$C = \pi d = \pi \times 5 = 15.71$
(rounded off to two decimal places)
Add the two lengths of the rectangle to the circumference of the circle.

Total perimeter = 15.71 + 10 + 10 = 35.71 ft

The perimeter of the deck is 35.71 ft.

**Calculate the perimeter of the following complex shapes.
Round off answers to two decimal places.**

1)   P =

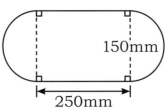

150mm

250mm

2)   P = $6.6' + 6.6' + 3.1416 \times 3.3'$

       $= 23.8053°$

       $= 23.81'$

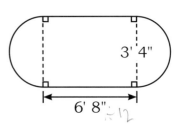

3' 4"

6' 8" ÷ 12

3)   P =

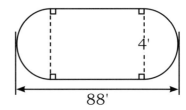

4'

88'

3.1416
is
PIE
always!!!

4)   P =

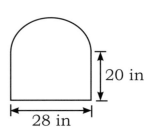

20 in

28 in

Bedmas!! ⊙ ⊙

5) P = $2 + 2 + 2\frac{5}{12}$

6.416' (3.146 × 2.416') ÷ 2 =

= 10.2117194.7

= 10.21'

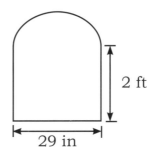

2 ft

29 in

6) P =

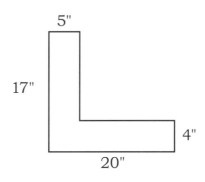

5"

17"

20"

4"

7) P =

$\begin{matrix} 1 \\ 6 \\ 5.5 \\ 5.5 \\ 2 \\ 3.5 \\ \hline 22.5\ m \end{matrix}$

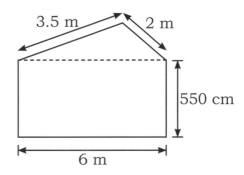

3.5 m   2 m

550 cm

6 m

8) $P = 3.1416 \times 1.6 \times .75 + 1.6$

$= 5.36992$

$= 5.37m$

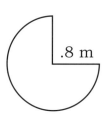

9) $P = \dfrac{3.1416 \times 9.25 + 9.25}{2}$

$= 23.7799$

$= 23.78"$

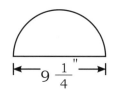

10) $P = 2.4 + 2.4 + (3.1416 \times 2.4 \div 2)$

$= 8.56992$

$= 8.57$

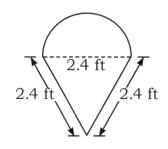

AREA

INTRODUCTION

Area is two-dimensional: length and width. In some math texts area is referred to as plane geometry. Area is always measured in square units. In this chapter, you will learn how to calculate the area of different shapes.

12" = 1'	144 in² = 1 ft²	1,728 in³ = 1 ft³
↓	↓	↓
perimeter	area	volume
One-dimensional	Two-dimensional	Three-dimensional
inches	in^2	in^3
feet	ft^2	ft^3
yards	yd^2	yd^3
mm	mm^2	mm^3
cm	cm^2	cm^3
m	m^2	m^3

When you have completed this chapter you will be able to:

❐ Calculate the area of rectangles, squares, triangles, circles, parallelograms, trapezoids and hexagons using formulas.

❐ Calculate the area of complex shapes using a combination of formulas.

❐ Calculate lateral area (L.A.) and surface area (S.A.) of cylinders and rectangular solids, square-based and triangular-based frustrums.

❐ Solve word problems using area.

❐ Solve applications using area.

CALCULATING AREA

Always use the same steps to solve area problems.

Step 1:   Draw a diagram and label it. All measurements must be in the same unit of measurement before you calculate area. Refer to the Measurements and Conversions chapter for help converting units.

Step 2:   Write the formula.

Step 3:   Calculate the area. Include the units of measurement as part of your answer.

Example 1:

Calculate the area of a floor that measures four metres long and two metres wide.

Step 1:   Draw a diagram and label it.

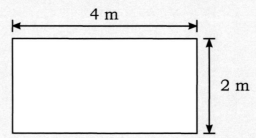

Step 2:   Write the formula.
A = LW

Step 3:   Calculate the area.
A = LW = 4 m × 2 m = 8 m²

The area of the floor is 8 m².

Example 2:

Calculate the area of a floor that measures 4 metres long and 350 centimetres wide.

Step 1:   Draw a diagram and label it.

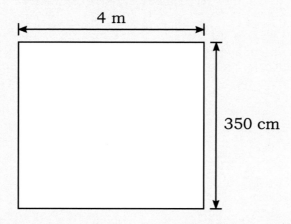

The two dimensions do not have the same unit of measurement. You need to convert metres to centimetres or centimetres to metres before you can calculate the area.

$$350 \text{ cm} = 3.5 \text{ m}$$

Step 2:   Write the formula.
            $A = LW$

Step 3:   Calculate the area.
            $A = LW = 4 \text{ m} \times 3.5 \text{ m} = 14 \text{ m}^2$

            The area of the floor is 14 m^2.

Calculate the area of the following figures. Round off to two decimal places. If your calculator doesn't have π, use 3.1416.

Remember:

Multiplying by a $\frac{1}{2}$ is the same as dividing by 2.

1) A =

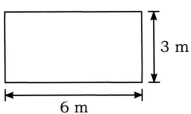

3 m

6 m

2) A =

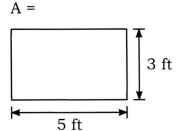

3 ft

5 ft

3) A =

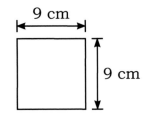

9 cm

9 cm

4) A =

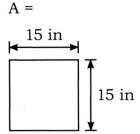

15 in

15 in

Hint:

Radius is half the diameter.

5) A =

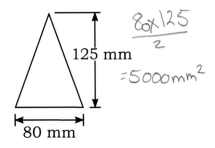

125 mm

80 mm

$\frac{80 \times 125}{2}$

$= 5000 mm^2$

6) A =

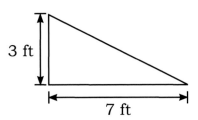

3 ft

7 ft

7) A = $3.1416 \times 4 \times 4$

$= 50.2656$

$= 50.27 m^2$

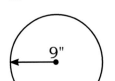

4 m

8) A =

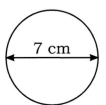

9"

9) A =

7 cm

10) A =

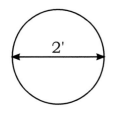

11) A =

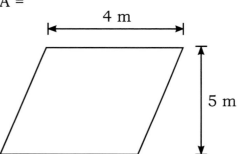

4 m

5 m

12) A = $6 \times 4 = 24 ft^2$

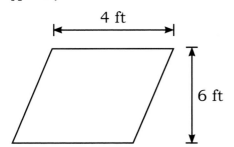

4 ft

6 ft

13) A =

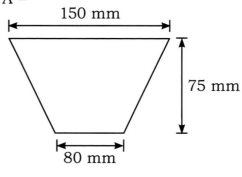

150 mm

75 mm

80 mm

14) A = $\dfrac{(9+4.5)}{2} \times 3 = \dfrac{13.5}{2} \times 3$

6.75×3

$= 20.25 ft^2$

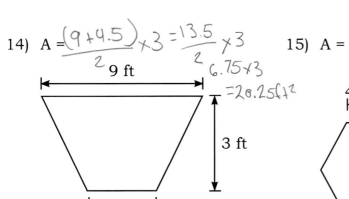

9 ft

3 ft

4.5 ft

15) A =

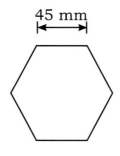

45 mm

16) A =

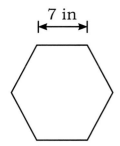

7 in

17) A =

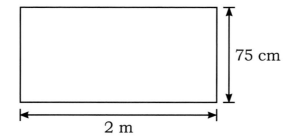

75 cm

2 m

18) A =

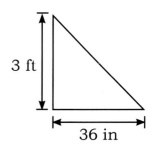

3 ft

36 in

19) A =

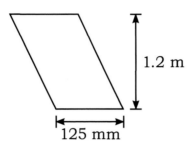

1.2 m

125 mm

20) A =

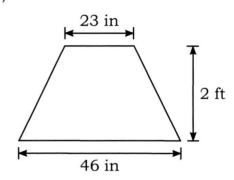

23 in

2 ft

46 in

21) A =

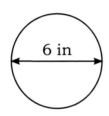

6 in

22) A =

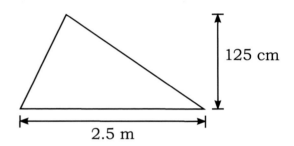

125 cm

2.5 m

23) A =

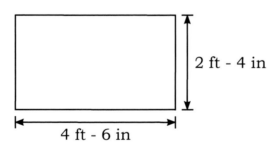

2 ft - 4 in

4 ft - 6 in

24) A =

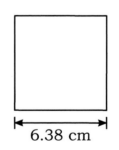

6.38 cm

25) A =

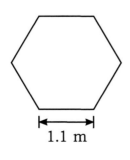

1.1 m

26) A =

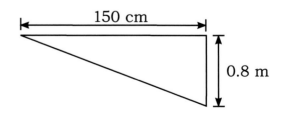

150 cm

0.8 m

CALCULATING THE AREA OF COMPLEX SHAPES

Sometimes you need to do several calculations to get the final answer. Many area problems are a combination of common geometrical shapes. To solve these problems, you will need to divide the drawing into shapes you are familiar with and calculate the area of each of those shapes. You might need to use the same formula several times or you might need to use several different formulas.

Example 1:

3.5 m

9 m

2 m

6.5 m

Calculate the area of the L-shaped room.

There are three different ways to solve this problem.

Steps	Method 1	Method 2	Method 3
Draw a diagram and label it.	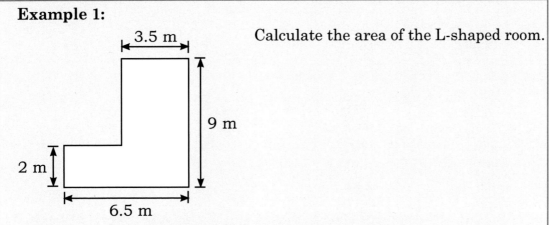		
Write the formula(s).	A = LW	A = LW	A = LW
Calculate the area.	Area 1: A = 3.5 × 7 = 24.5 m² Area 2: A = 6.5 × 2 = 13 m² Total Area = 13 m² + 24.5 m² = 37.5 m²	Area 1: A = 3.5 × 9 = 31.5 m² Area 2: A = 3 × 2 = 6 m² Total Area = 31.5 m² + 6 m² = 37.5 m²	Area 1: A = 6.5 × 9 = 58.5 m² Area 2: A = 3 × 7 = 21 m² Total Area = 58.5 – 21 = 37.5 m²

Remember:

There is often more than one way to solve a math problem.

Example 2:

Calculate the area of the deck.

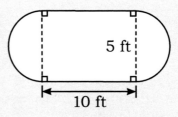

Step 1: Draw a diagram and label it.
Decide what basic shapes make up the diagram.

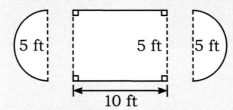

The two half-circles make one complete circle. You need to calculate the area of a circle plus the area of the rectangle.

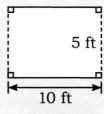

Step 2: Write the formula(s) you need to solve the problem.
Rectangle
$A = LW$
Circle
$A = \pi r^2$

Step 3: Calculate the area.
Calculate the area of a rectangle. Calculate the area of the circle. Calculate the total area by adding area of the rectangle and the area of the circle.
Rectangle
$A = LW = 10 \text{ ft} \times 5 \text{ ft} = 50 \text{ ft}^2$
Circle
The formula for area of a circle uses the radius. You need to divide the diameter by two to get the radius.
$5 \div 2 = 2.5 \text{ ft}$
$A = \pi r^2 = \pi \times (2.5)^2 = 19.6 \text{ ft}^2$

Total Area = 50 ft² + 19.6 ft² = 69.6 ft²
The area of the deck is 69.6 ft².

Example 3:

Sometimes it is easier to calculate the area of the empty space and subtract it from the total area than it is to calculate the area of a lot of little shapes and add them up.

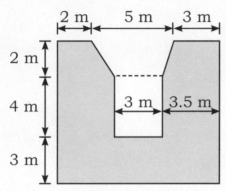

Step 1:   Draw a diagram and label it.

Think about the easiest way to calculate the area. As you can see there is more than one way to calculate the total area. Method 1 is easier because there are fewer calculations.

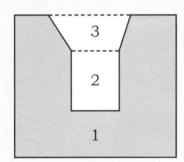

Method 1: Calculate three areas.

Calculate the area of 1.

Calculate the area of 2.

Calculate the area of 3.

Subtract the total area of 2 and 3 from 1.

The example illustrates Method 1.

Method 2:   Calculate 5 areas.

Calculate the area of 1 and 2.

Calculate the area of 3, 4 and 5.

Add 1, 2, 3, 4 and 5 to get the total area.

Step 2:   Write the formula(s) you need to solve the problem. Decide what basic shapes make up the diagram. In this example there are two basic shapes: rectangle and trapezoid.

Area 1 and Area 2:

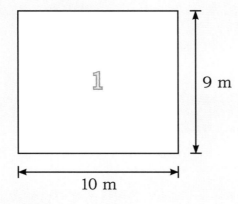

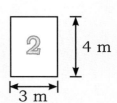

A = LW

Area 3:

$A = \left(\frac{b_1 + b_2}{2}\right)h$

Step 3:   Calculate the area.

Area 1:

$A = LW = 9 \times 10 = 90 \text{ m}^2$

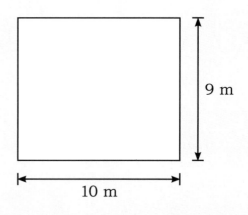

Area 2:

$A = LW = 4 \times 3 = 12 \text{ m}^2$

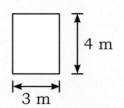

Area 3:

$$A = \left(\frac{b_1 + b_2}{2}\right)h = \left(\frac{5 + 3}{2}\right)2 = \left(\frac{8}{2}\right)2 = (4)2 = 8 \text{ m}^2$$

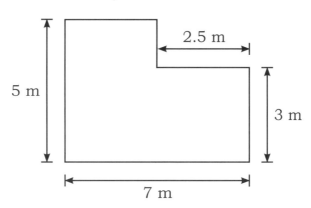

Subtract the area of the trapezoid and the small rectangle from the big rectangle to get the total area.

Total Area = 90 − (12 + 8) = 90 − 20 = 70 m²
The area of shaded diagram is 70 m².

Calculate the area of the following shapes. If the shapes have shading calculate the area that is shaded. Round off to two decimal places. If your calculator doesn't have π, use 3.1416.

1)   A =

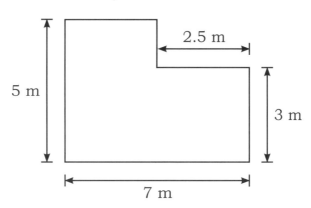

2)   A =

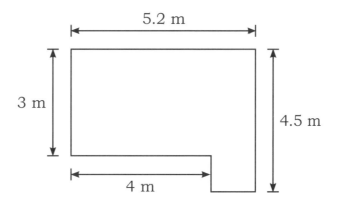

3)   A =

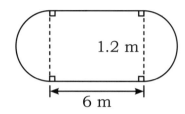

4)   A =

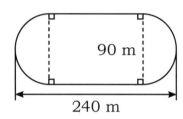

5)   A =

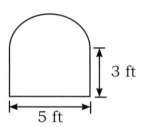

6)   A =

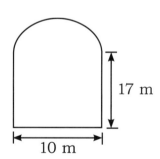

7) A =

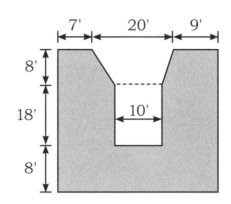

8) A =

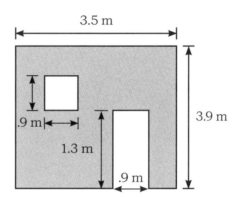

Hint:

Read the diagram
carefully. Decide
what basic geometric
shapes are used.
Decide if it is easier
to subtract or add to
calculate the
total area.

9) A =

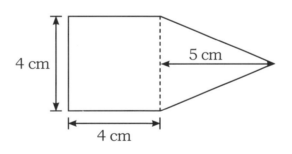

10) A =

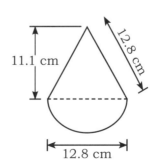

11) A =

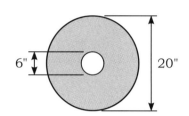

12) A =

8.44
2.14
2.14
_____
12.72

$\dfrac{(12.72+8.44)}{2} \times 3.88 + 8.44 \times \dfrac{2.38}{2}$ = 41.0504 + 6.0436

$\dfrac{21.16}{2} \times 3.88 + 10.0436$ = 51.094

= 51.09 m²

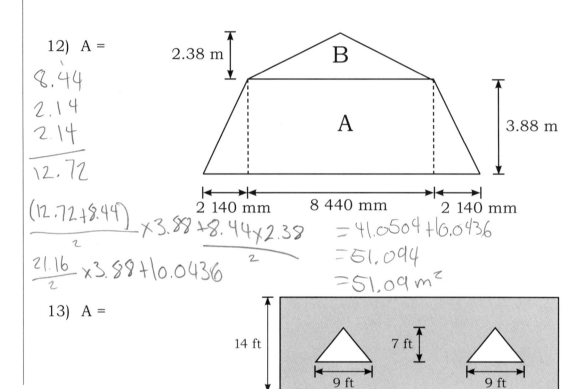

13) A =

14) A =

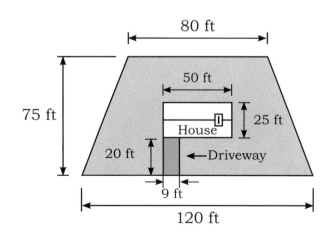

15) A =

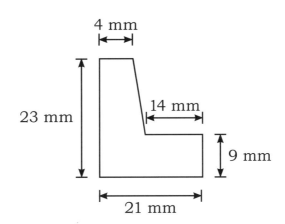

16) A =

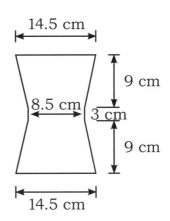

17) A =

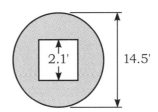

18) A =

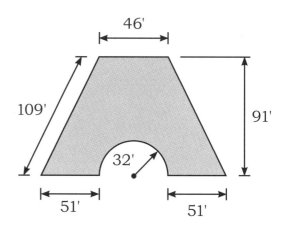

19) A =

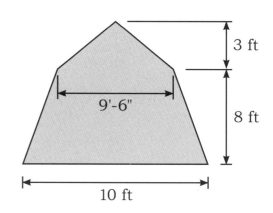

20) A = $3.1416 \times 256 \times 250 - (3.1416 \times 125 \times 125 + 3.1416 \times (5 \times 15 \times 8)$

= 196350 - (49087.5 + 5654.88)

= 19635 - 54742.38

= 14167.62 mm²

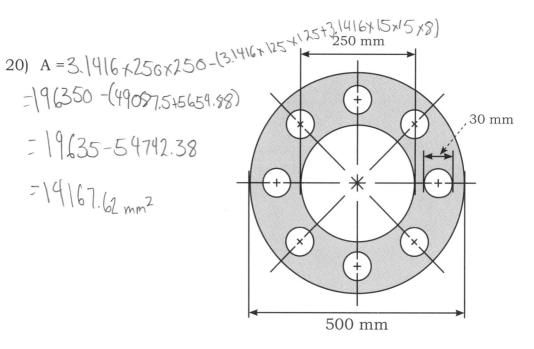

CALCULATING ONE OF THE SIDES WHEN YOU KNOW THE AREA

Sometimes you know the area of a shape and need to work backwards to calculate one of the sides. You work with the same formula(s).

Step 1:   Draw a diagram and label it with the known information.

Step 2:   Write the formula(s) required.

Step 3:   Calculate the side.

Example 1:

Calculate the length of the rectangle in the diagram below.

Step 1:   Draw a diagram and label it with the known information.

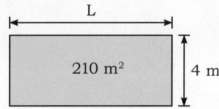

Step 2:   Write the formula(s) required.
$A = LW$

Step 3:   Calculate the side.
$A = LW$
$210 \text{ m}^2 = L \times 4 \text{ m}$

$$\frac{210}{4} = L$$

$$\frac{210}{4} = 52.5$$

The length of the side is 52.5 m.

Example 2:

Calculate the diameter of the circle in the diagram below.

Step 1: Draw a diagram and label it with the known information.

Step 2: Write the formula(s) required.

$$A = \pi r^2$$

Step 3: Calculate the diameter.

Note: If your calculator doesn't have π, use 3.1416.

$$A = \pi r^2$$

$$\frac{25}{\pi} = r^2$$

$$7.96 = r^2$$

$$\sqrt{7.96} = r$$

$$2.82 = r$$

The radius is 2.82 ft. You were asked to calculate the diameter. Diameter is equal to two times the radius.

$D = 2.82 \times 2 = 5.64$
The diameter of the circle is 5.64 ft.

Calculate the missing side in the shapes below. Round off to two decimal places. If your calculator doesn't have π, use 3.1416.

1) Calculate the length of the rectangle.

L =

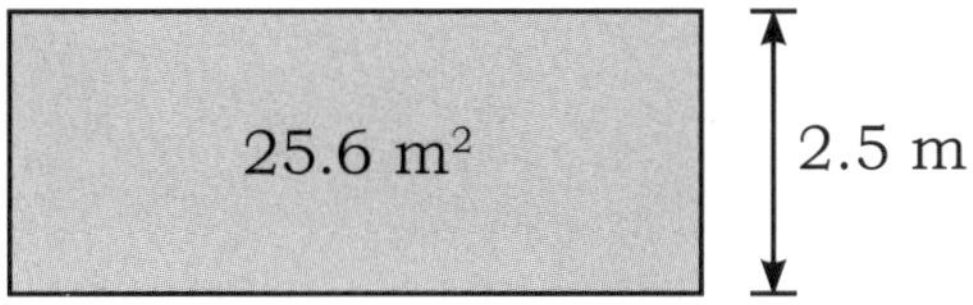

25.6 m²   2.5 m

2) Calculate the width of the rectangle.

W =

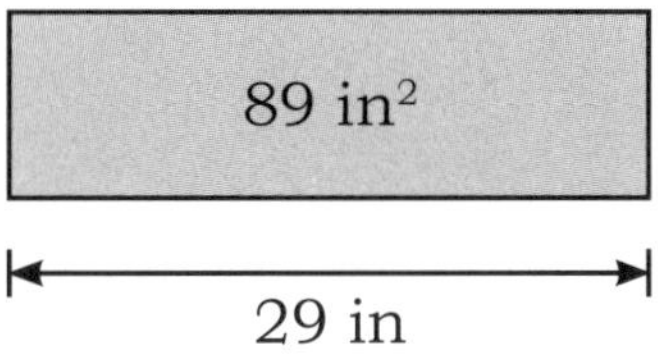

89 in²

29 in

3) Calculate the radius of the circle.

r =

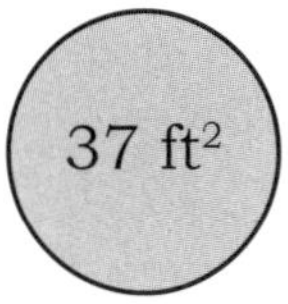

37 ft²

4) Calculate the diameter of the circle.

d =

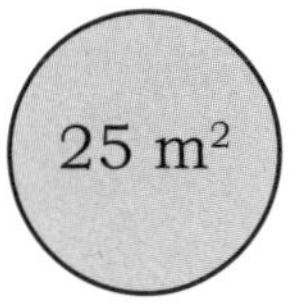

25 m²

5) Calculate the base of the triangle.

b =

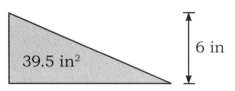

6) Calculate the height of the triangle.

h =

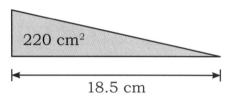

7) Calculate the side of the square.

s =

355 cm^2

8) Calculate the side of the square.

s =

415 ft^2

LATERAL AREA AND SURFACE AREA

Lateral Area (L.A.) is the area of all the surfaces except for the bases.

Cylinders   Rectangular solids

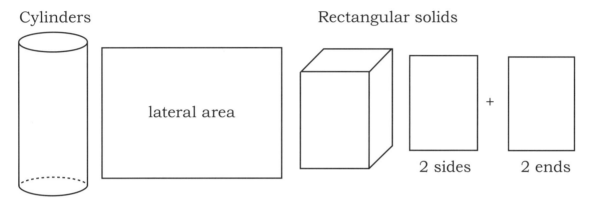

Surface Area (S.A.) is the lateral area plus the area of the two bases.

Cylinders   Rectangular solids

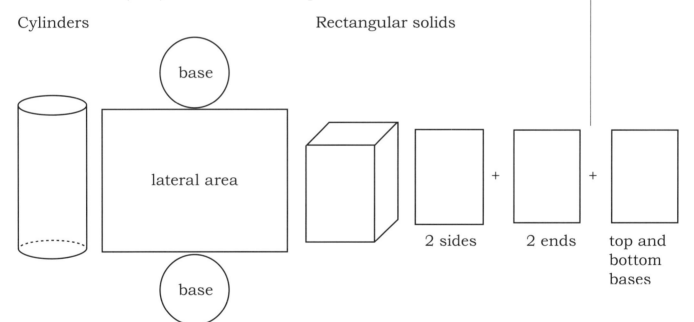

Example 1:

Calculate the lateral surface area (L.A.) and total surface area (S.A.) of a cylinder that is 6 m high and has a diameter of 2.5 m.

Lateral Area

Step 1:   Draw a diagram and label it.

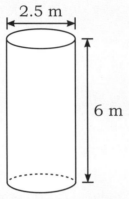

Step 2:   Write the formula needed to solve the problem.

L.A. = πd × h

Think of the cylinder as being laid out flat, so the circumference becomes the width measurement.

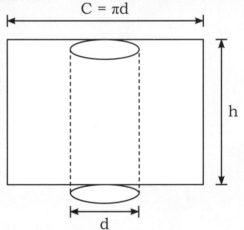

Step 3:   Calculate the lateral area.

L.A. = πd × h = π × 2.5 m × 6 m = 47.12 m²

Surface area:

Step 1: Draw a diagram and label it.

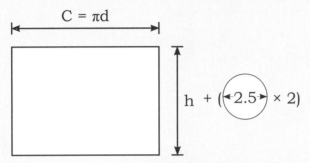

$C = \pi d$

$h + (2.5 \times 2)$

Step 2: Write the formula needed to solve the problem.
S.A. = L.A. + area of the two bases
You have already calculated the L.A.

The two bases are circles. Calculate the area of a circle and multiply by 2 because there are two identical circles.

Radius = diameter ÷ 2 = 2.5 m ÷ 2 = 1.25 m

S.A. = L.A. + area of two bases =
$47.12 \text{ m}^2 + (\pi r^2 \times 2) = 47.12 \text{ m}^2 + (\pi \times (1.25 \text{ m})^2 \times 2) =$
$47.12 \text{ m}^2 + 9.04 \text{ m}^2 = 56.16 \text{ m}^2$

Remember:

BEDMAS.

Example 2:

Calculate the lateral area (L.A.) and total surface area (S.A.) of the rectangular solid below.

Lateral Area

Step 1: Draw a diagram and label it.

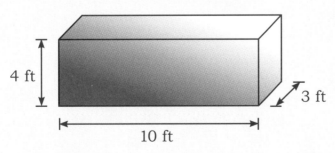

4 ft

3 ft

10 ft

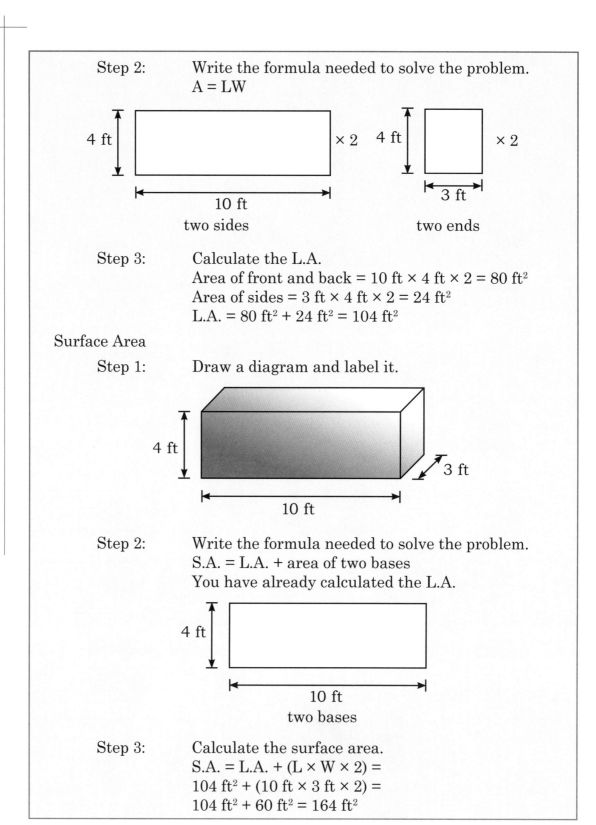

Step 2: Write the formula needed to solve the problem.
A = LW

4 ft   × 2   4 ft   × 2

10 ft
two sides   3 ft
two ends

Step 3: Calculate the L.A.
Area of front and back = 10 ft × 4 ft × 2 = 80 ft^2
Area of sides = 3 ft × 4 ft × 2 = 24 ft^2
L.A. = 80 ft^2 + 24 ft^2 = 104 ft^2

Surface Area
Step 1: Draw a diagram and label it.

4 ft   3 ft

10 ft

Step 2: Write the formula needed to solve the problem.
S.A. = L.A. + area of two bases
You have already calculated the L.A.

4 ft

10 ft
two bases

Step 3: Calculate the surface area.
S.A. = L.A. + (L × W × 2) =
104 ft^2 + (10 ft × 3 ft × 2) =
104 ft^2 + 60 ft^2 = 164 ft^2

**Calculate the lateral area and surface area of the shapes below.
Round off answers to two decimal places.**

1)   L.A. =

      S.A. =

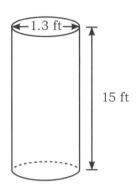

2)   L.A. =

      S.A. =

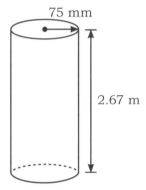

3)   L.A. =

      S.A. =

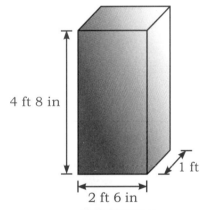

4)   L.A. =

      S.A. =

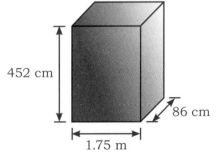

PRACTICE

Complete the following practice problems. Round off answers to two decimal places.

1) Calculate the cost of paving a driveway that measures 6 ft by 15 ft at $5.25 per square foot.

2) Calculate the surface area of the window below.

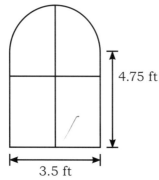

4.75 ft

3.5 ft

3) How many square metres of floor space are there in a circular silo that has a diameter of 12 m?

4) a) Calculate the square feet of drywall required for a room that measures 8 ft by 10 ft. The walls are 9 ft high. There are two doors that measure 3 ft by 7 ft and one window that measures 2.5 ft by 4 ft.

Hint:

There are four walls.

b) One sheet of drywall measures 4 ft by 8 ft and costs $38.98. Calculate the total cost.

Hint:

Can't buy part of a sheet of drywall.

5) Calculate the square feet of plywood required to make five cupboards like the one in the diagram below.

Hint:

You are calculating the surface area.

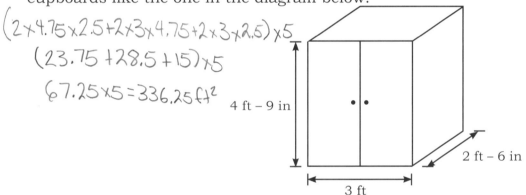

$(2 \times 4.75 \times 2.5 + 2 \times 3 \times 4.75 + 2 \times 3 \times 2.5) \times 5$

$(23.75 + 28.5 + 15) \times 5$

$67.25 \times 5 = 336.25 \, ft^2$

4 ft – 9 in

2 ft – 6 in

3 ft

6) How many square feet of pine are required to line a closet that measures 6.5 feet wide, 4.5 feet deep and 8 feet high? Allow 21 square feet for the door.

Hint:

You are calculating the surface area.

7) The roof shown in the diagram below is to be covered with asphalt shingles. Calculate the square feet of surface to be covered.

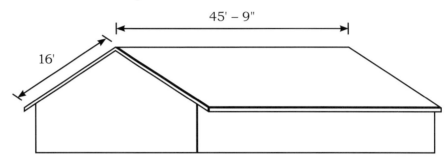

8) Calculate the cost of 36 pieces of paneling 4 ft × 8 ft. The panelling costs $1.25 per square foot.

VOLUME

INTRODUCTION

Volume is three-dimensional. It is the amount of space inside an object or the amount of space an object occupies. Volume is always measured in cubic units. In this chapter, you will learn how to calculate the volume of different solids.

It is important you understand the difference between perimeter, area and volume, and how each is measured. The table below compares perimeter, area and volume.

$12" = 1'$	$144 \text{ in}^2 = 1 \text{ ft}^2$	$1,728 \text{ in}^3 = 1 \text{ ft}^3$
↓	↓	↓
perimeter	area	volume
One-dimensional	Two-dimensional	Three-dimensional
inches	in^2	in^3
feet	ft^2	ft^3
yards	yd^2	yd^3
mm	mm^2	mm^3
cm	cm^2	cm^3
m	m^2	m^3

At the end of this chapter you will be able to:

❐ Calculate the volume of simple and complex shapes.

❐ Solve word problems using volume.

❐ Solve applications using volume.

CALCULATING VOLUME

Always use the same steps to solve volume problems.

Step 1: Draw a diagram and label it. All measurements must be in the same unit of measurement before you calculate volume. Refer to the Measurements and Conversions chapter for help converting units.

Step 2: Write the formula.

Step 3: Calculate the volume. Include the units of measurement as part of your answer.

Example 1:

Calculate the volume of a rectangular solid that measures 6 m long, 5 m wide and 2 m high.

Step 1: Draw a diagram and label it.

2 m
6 m
5 m

Step 2: Write the formula.
V = LWH

Step 3: Calculate the volume.
V = LWH = 6 × 5 × 2 = 60 m³

The volume is 60 m³.

Example 2:

Calculate the volume of a cylinder that has a radius of 2 ft and a height of 6 ft.

Step 1: Draw a diagram and label it.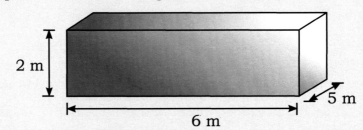

Step 2: Write the formula.
V = πr²h

Step 3: Calculate the volume.

2 ft

6 ft

Note: If your calculator doesn't have π, use 3.1416. Your answer will be slightly different because it is slightly less accurate.

$V = \pi r^2 h = \pi \times 2^2 \times 6 = 75.4 \text{ ft}^3$.
(rounded to the nearest tenth)

The volume of the cylinder is 75.4 ft³.

Example 3:

Step 1: Draw a diagram and label it.

Step 2: Write the formula.

$V = \dfrac{\pi r^2 h}{3}$

84 cm   80 cm

25 cm

Note: The formula requires the height of the cone. Height is the perpendicular measurement from the base to the top of the cone. Make sure you use the height and not the slant height.

Step 3: Calculate the volume.

$V = \dfrac{\pi r^2 h}{3} = \dfrac{\pi \times 25^2 \times 80}{3} = \dfrac{157\,079.6}{3} = 52\,359.9 \text{ cm}^3$

The volume of the cone is 52 359.9 cm³.

Calculate the volume of the following solids. Round off answers to two decimal places. If your calculator doesn't have π, use 3.1416.

1) V =

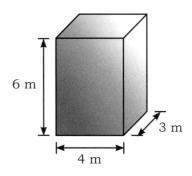

2) V =

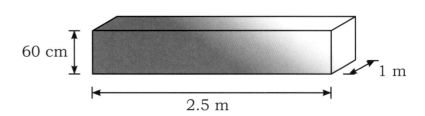

3) V =

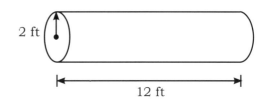

4) V =

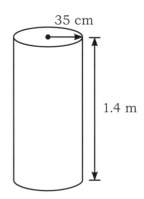

5) V =

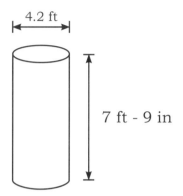

4.2 ft

7 ft - 9 in

6) V =

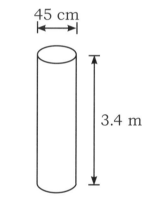

45 cm

3.4 m

7) V =

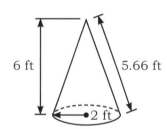

6 ft

5.66 ft

2 ft

8) V =

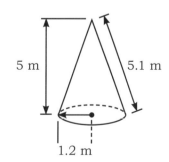

5 m

5.1 m

1.2 m

9) V =

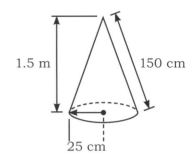

1.5 m · 150 cm · 25 cm

10) V =

2 ft

11) V =

75 cm

12) V =

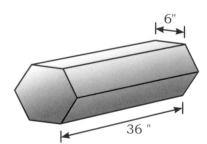

6" · 36 "

13) V =

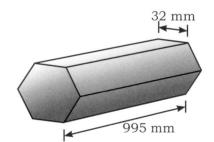

32 mm · 995 mm

14) V =

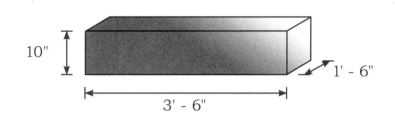

10"

3' - 6"

1' - 6"

15) V =

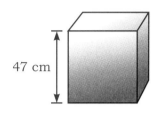

47 cm

16) V =

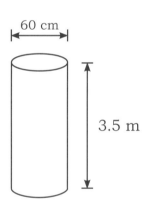

60 cm

3.5 m

17) V =

-3.2 ft-

18) V =

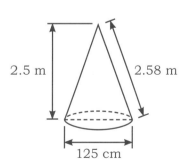

2.5 m

2.58 m

125 cm

19) V =

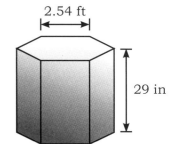

20) V =

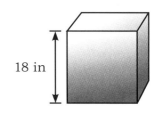

CALCULATING THE VOLUME OF COMPLEX SHAPES

Sometimes you need to do more than one calculation or use more than one formula to calculate volume because the solid is a combination of shapes. You will need to divide the solid into shapes you are familiar with and calculate the volume of each of those shapes. To get the total volume, you will need to add or subtract the volume of each of the shapes. You may need to use the same formula several times or you may need to use more than one formula. The steps for calculating the volume of a complex shape are the same.

Example 1:

A concrete wall and footing are poured at the same time. Calculate the volume of concrete that is needed. Look at the diagram below.

Step 1:   Draw a diagram and label it.

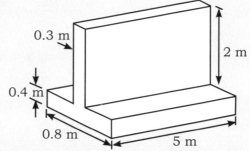

Step 2:   Write the formula(s).
Think of the shape as being two rectangular solids called A and B.

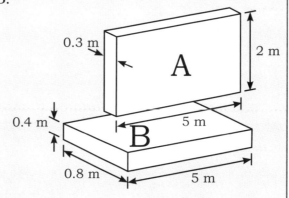

V = LWH

Step 3:   Calculate the volume.
Volume of wall = LWH = 5 m × .3 m × 2 = 3 m³
Volume of footing = LWH = 5 m × .8 m × .4 m = 1.6 m³

Total Volume = 1.6 m³ + 3 m³ = 4.6 m³
The volume of the concrete wall and footing is 4.6 m³.

Example 2:

Calculate the volume of the concrete figure below.

Step 1: Draw a diagram and label it.

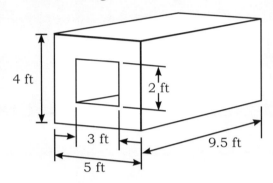

Step 2: Write the formula(s).
V = LWH

Step 3: Calculate the volume.
Big volume = LWH = 9.5 ft × 5 ft × 4 ft = 190 ft^3
Small volume = LWH = 9.5 ft × 3 ft × 2 ft = 57 ft^3

Total Volume = 190 ft^3 – 57 ft^3 = 133 ft^3
The volume of the concrete figure is 133 ft^3.

Calculate the volume of the following solids. Round off answers to two decimal places. If your calculator doesn't have π, use 3.1416.

1) V =

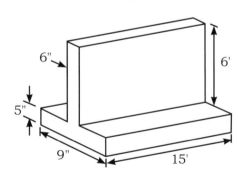

2) V =

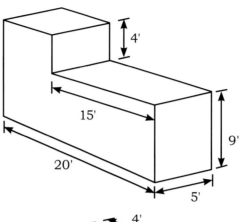

3) V =

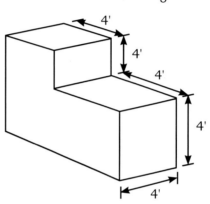

Hint:

A wedge is a
rectangular solid
cut diagonally in
half.

4) V =

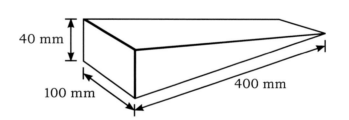

5) V =

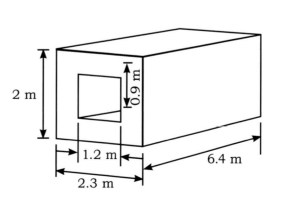

Hint:

Read the diagram carefully. Decide what shapes are used.

6)   V =

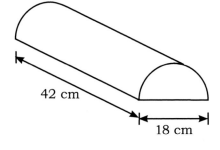
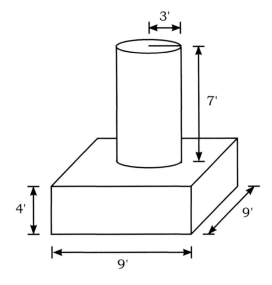

7)   V =

8)   V =

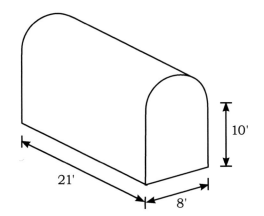

9) V =

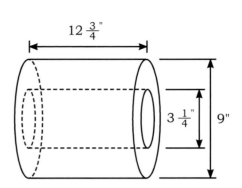

10) V =

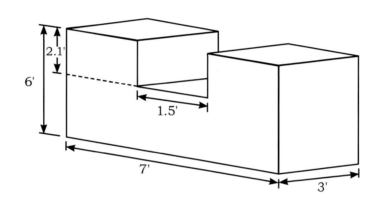

11) V =

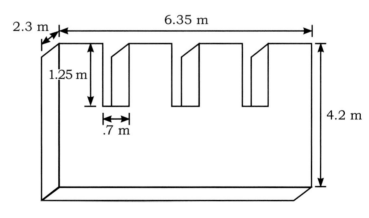

12) V =

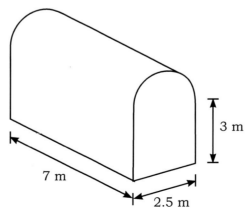

13) V =

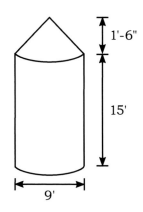

14) V =

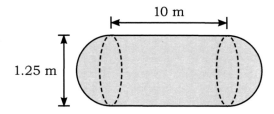

15) V =

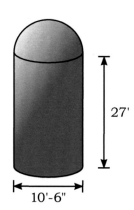

CALCULATING THE HEIGHT OR DIAMETER WHEN YOU KNOW THE VOLUME

Sometimes you know the volume of a shape and need to work backwards to calculate one of the sides or the diameter. You work with the same formula(s).

Step 1: Draw a diagram and label it with the known information.

Step 2: Write the formula(s) required.

Step 3: Calculate the side.

Example 1:

Calculate the length of the rectangular solid in the diagram below.

Step 1: Draw a diagram and label it with the known information.

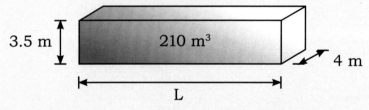

Step 2: Write the formula(s) required.
$V = LWH$

Step 3: Calculate the side.
$V = LWH$
$210 \text{ m}^3 = L \times 4 \times 3.5$
$210 \text{ m}^3 = L \times 14$

$$\frac{210}{14} = L$$

$$\frac{210}{14} = 15$$

The length of the side is 15 m.

Example 2:

Calculate the radius of the cylinder in the diagram below.

Step 1: Draw a diagram and label it with the known information.

Step 2: Write the formula(s) required.
$V = \pi r^2 h$

Step 3: Calculate the radius.
$V = \pi r^2 h$
$25 \text{ ft}^2 = \pi r^2 \times 4.2 \text{ ft}$

$\dfrac{25}{4.2} = \pi r^2$

$5.95 = \pi r^2$

$\dfrac{5.95}{\pi} = r^2$

$1.89 = r^2$

$\sqrt{1.89} = r$
$1.38 = r$

The radius of the cylinder is 1.38 ft.

Calculate the missing side in the shapes below. Round off to two decimal places. If your calculator doesn't have π, use 3.1416.

1) Calculate the height of the rectangular solid.

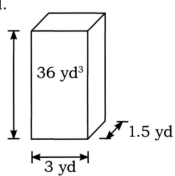

2) Calculate the width of the rectangular solid.

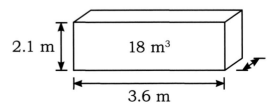

3)   Calculate the radius of the cylinder.

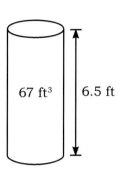

67 ft³   6.5 ft

4)   Calculate the height of the cylinder.

22 in

188 in³

5)   Calculate the diameter of the cylinder.

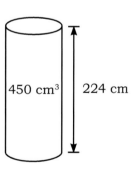

450 cm³   224 cm

6)   Calculate the height of the cone.

234 ft³

10 ft

7)   Calculate the diameter of the cone.

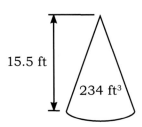

15.5 ft

234 ft³

PRACTICE

Round up answers to the nearest whole yd³ or m³.

1)   How many cubic yards of concrete are needed for a driveway
      section that measures 6 yards long, 3 yards wide, and 1 foot thick?

2)   Calculate the volume of concrete needed in cubic metres to fill a
      form that measures 3 m high by 400 mm wide by 12 m long.

3)   A carpenter needs to pour a rectangular slab that is 13 m long,
      6 m wide, and 0.3 m thick. Calculate the volume.

Hint:

1 yd³ = 27 ft³

4)   Calculate the volume of fill in cubic yards required to fill a hole
      5.5 ft long, 2 ft wide and 3.6 ft deep. Add 30% to allow for compaction.

5) A pile of gravel is in the shape of a cone. The diameter of the pile is 6.5 m and the height is 2.3 m. How many cubic metres of gravel are in the pile?

6) How many cubic yards of concrete are needed to pour a concrete retaining wall that measures 39 feet long by 1.6 feet wide by 5 feet high?

7) Calculate the cubic meters of concrete needed to fill 8 cylindrical forms that are the same size. The radius measures 0.4 m and the height is 4.5 m.   3.1416 x. 4x.4 x 4.5 x 8
= 18.095616 m³

8) Nine footings are required to support nine steel columns. How many cubic yards of concrete are needed to pour nine footings that are 24" × 24" × 24"?

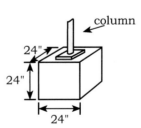

column

24"

24"

24"

÷27!!

9) Calculate the cubic yards of concrete needed to fill the stair form shown below.

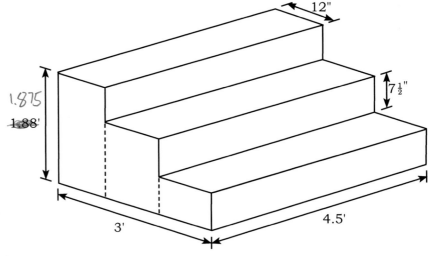

1.875
1.88'

12"

7½"

3'

4.5'

$1.875 \times 2 \times 4.5$

$= 16.875 ft^3 \div 27 = 0.625 yd^3$

10) Fill is needed for an excavation that measures 9 feet long by 15 feet wide by 6.4 feet deep. Calculate the amount of available fill piled in a cone shape that has a 12 foot diameter and is 7 feet high. Calculate the cubic yards of additional fill the contractor needs to order. Allow for 25% compaction.

11) The fill excavated for a swimming pool must be hauled away. A truck has a capacity for 27 yd³. How many truckloads have to be hauled away?

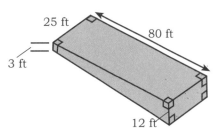

25 ft

80 ft

3 ft

12 ft

12) Calculate the cubic yards of earth that must be removed for the excavation shown below. The excavation is 8.5 ft. deep. A truck has a capacity for 27 yd³. How many truckloads of earth have to be hauled away?

Hint:

27 ft³ = 1 yd³

75'

40'

40'   40'

145'

$145 \times 75 - 40 \times 65$

$= 10875 - 2600$

$= 8275 \times 8.5 \div 27 = 2605.092593 \div 27$

$= 96.48491084$

$= 97$ truckloads.

RIGHT-ANGLE TRIANGLES

Trades workers often use the 3:4:5 Method, Pythagorean Theorem and trigonometry. The 3:4:5 Method is used to calculate the length of a missing side when the length of two sides is known and to check if corners are square. The Pythagorean Theorem is used to calculate the third side of a right-angle triangle when the length of two sides is known. Trigonometry is used to lay out job sites, to calculate the lengths and heights of things when direct measurements cannot be taken and to calculate the size of angles.

When you have finished this section you will be able to:

- ❏ Define and recognise common angles.
- ❏ Calculate the size of the missing angle in a triangle.
- ❏ Add and subtract degrees, minutes and seconds.
- ❏ Use the 3:4:5 Rule (Pythagorean Theorem) to calculate the length of the missing side in a right angle triangle.
- ❏ Locate opposite and adjacent sides in reference to a specific angle.
- ❏ Calculate the length of a side when an angle and one side are known.
- ❏ Calculate an angle when two sides are known.
- ❏ Solve word problems using the 3:4:5 Method and trigonometry.
- ❏ Solve applications using the 3:4:5 Method and trigonometry.

ANGLES

An angle is formed when two straight lines meet to form a corner. This corner is called the vertex.

Vertex — An Angle

Nail — Angle

An angle describes how much something turns or rotates. For example, if you put a nail through a board, and then rotate the board around the nail, you could say the board turned through an angle.

The amount of turning is the size of the angle. Angles are measured in degrees. An angle of forty-five degrees is written as 45°.

Protractors, steel squares, transits, or special triangles are used in construction to find the number of degrees in an angle.

Basic Angles

You should be able to identify the angles below and use that information to solve other problems.

One full turn = 360°

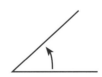

One half turn = 180°
Note: also called a straight angle

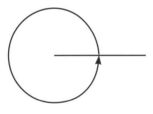

One quarter turn = 90°
Note: also called a right angle

One eighth turn = 45°

Intersecting Lines, Opposite Angles and Parallel Lines

- When 2 lines intersect or cross, the opposite angles are equal.

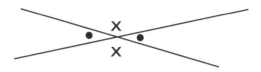

- Two straight lines are parallel when they run in exactly the same direction and do not cross at any point.

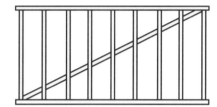

- If 2 parallel lines are crossed by a third line, the angles between the parallel lines that are diagonal to each other are equal. The third line is called a transversal.

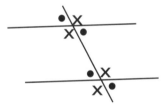

Labelling Angles in Triangles

All triangles have three angles. To be able to identify a specific angle in the triangle, the angles need to be labelled or named. Angles can be labelled:

- by number - ∠3

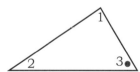

- by a single letter - ∠B

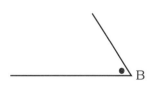

- by letters - ∠ABC

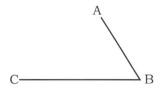

Answer the following questions about triangles.

1) Look at the triangle. Write the two other ways the angle can be named.

a) ∠ 2

b) ∠XYZ

c) ∠3

d) ∠1

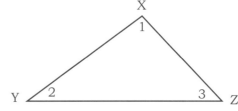

2) Calculate the number of degrees in each of the following.

a) ∠ 7 + ∠8 + ∠9 =

b) ∠8 + ∠9 + ∠10 =

c) ∠11 + ∠7 =

d) ∠7 + ∠8 + ∠9 + ∠10 + ∠11 =

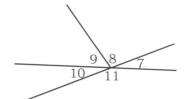

3) Write in the number of degrees in each of the marked angles.

a)

b)

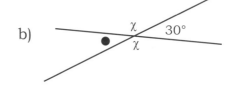

c)

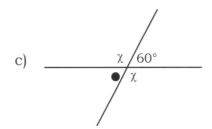

d)

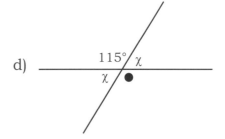

4) Write the number of degrees in each of the following named angles.

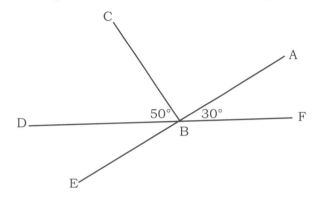

Hint:

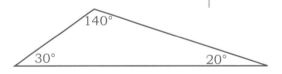 means 90°

a) ∠DBE =

b) ∠FBD =

c) ∠ABF + ∠ABC + ∠CBD =

d) ∠ABC =

e) ∠ABC + ∠CBD =

f) ∠ABC + ∠CBD + ∠FBE =

Calculating the Missing Angle in a Triangle

If two angles in a triangle are known, the third can be easily calculated.
The three angles in a triangle always add up to 180°.

∠1 + ∠2 + ∠3 = 180°

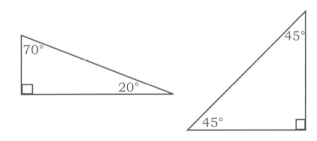

Calculate the missing angle in each of the following triangles.

1)

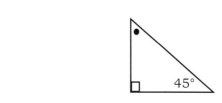

2)

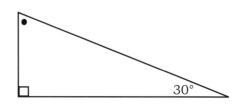

3)

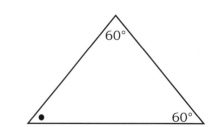

4)

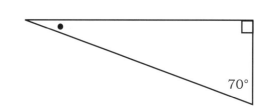

5)

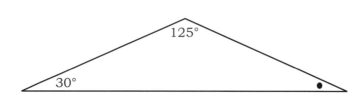

6)

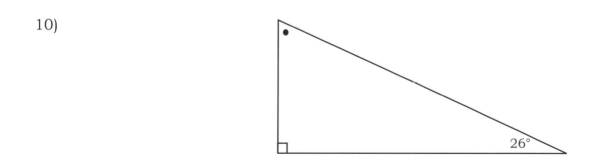

7)

8)

9)

10)

Calculating Degrees, Minutes and Seconds

Angles are measured in degrees (degrees of arc), minutes (minutes of arc) and seconds (seconds of arc). When you are surveying or working with a transit on a job site, you will need to use units that are smaller than 1°.

$$60" \text{ (seconds)} = 1' \text{ (minute)}$$

$$60' \text{ (minutes)} = 1° \text{ (degree)}$$

$$3\ 600" \text{ (seconds)} = 1° \text{ (degree)}$$

> **Hint:** Even though the symbols for seconds and minutes are the same as the symbols for inches and feet, and the words 'seconds' and 'minutes are used for time measurement, there shouldn't be any confusion. It should be clear from the situation if you are talking about angle measurement, length measurement, or time measurement.

Example 1:

Change 65" to minutes and seconds.

$$65" = 60" + 5" = 1' + 5" = 1'\ 5"$$

Example 2:

Change 152' to degrees and minutes.

$$
\begin{array}{r}
2 \\
60\overline{)152} \\
-120 \\
\hline
32
\end{array}
$$

$$152' = 2°\ 32'$$

Change the following seconds to minutes and seconds.

1) a) 61"   b) 119"   c) 72"   d) 112"

2) a) 180"   b) 183"   c) 77"   d) 242"

Change the following minutes to degrees and minutes.

1) a) 61' b) 119' c) 47' d) 80'

2) a) 110' b) 95' c) 255' d) 60'

Adding and Subtracting Angles

Example 1:

$$
\begin{array}{rrrr}
 & 23° & 14' & 32'' \\
+ & 12° & 55' & 41'' \\
\end{array}
$$

Step 1: Add the seconds.
$$
\begin{array}{rrrr}
 & 23° & 14' & 32'' \\
+ & 12° & 55' & 41'' \\
\hline
 & & & 73'' \\
\end{array}
$$

Step 2: Add the minutes.
$$
\begin{array}{rrrr}
 & 23° & 14' & 32'' \\
+ & 12° & 55' & 41'' \\
\hline
 & & 69' & 73'' \\
\end{array}
$$

Step 3: Add the degrees.
$$
\begin{array}{rrrr}
 & 23° & 14' & 32'' \\
+ & 12° & 55' & 41'' \\
\hline
 & 35° & 69' & 73'' \\
\end{array}
$$

Step 4: Simplify any seconds or minutes amount that is larger than 60.

73'' = 1' 13''

35° 69' 73''

Convert the seconds. 1' 13''

35° 70' 13''

1° 10'

Convert the minutes. 36° 10' 13''

RIGHT-ANGLE TRIANGLES

Add the following.

Remember:

1' = 60"
1° = 60'

1)
```
   24° 19' 32"
 + 18° 32' 16"
```

2)
```
   4°  0' 42"
 + 5°  2'  8"
```

3)
```
   71° 14' 28"
 +  5° 18' 51"
```

4)
```
   77° 45' 54"
 + 28°  6' 17"
```

5)
```
   85° 51' 15"
 +  4°  8' 45"
```

6)
```
   42° 45' 19"
 +  5° 27' 52"
```

7)
```
   41° 45' 19"
 + 35° 14' 38"
```

8)
```
   74°  0' 51"
 + 19°  0' 42"
```

9)
```
   26° 32'  0"
 + 45° 47'  0"
```

10)
```
   15° 57' 21"
 + 18° 44' 41"
```

11)
```
   55° 44' 11"
 + 88° 33' 22"
```

12)
```
   89° 59' 59"
 + 90°  0'  1"
```

13)
```
    96° 19'
 + 152° 21'
```

14)
```
   32° 43' 14"
 + 47° 17' 58"
```

15)
```
   179° 58' 56"
 +        1'  4"
```

16)
```
   21° 46' 34"
 + 18° 21' 27"
```

Subtracting Angles

Example 1:

```
   45° 16' 39"
 − 22°  3' 13"
```

Step 1:   Subtract the seconds.
```
   45° 16' 39"
 − 22°  3' 13"
           26"
```

Step 2:   Subtract the minutes.
```
   45° 16' 39"
 − 22°  3' 13"
       13' 26"
```

Step 3:   Subtract the degrees.
```
   45° 16' 39"
 − 22°  3' 13"
   23° 13' 26"
```

Borrowing

Example 2:

$$\begin{array}{r} 27°\ 35'\ 12" \\ -\ 13°\ 11'\ 42" \end{array}$$

Step 1: Subtract the seconds.
You can't subtract 42 from 12
so borrow one from the minutes.
Change 35 to 34. One minute
equals 60 seconds. Add 60 to 12.
Now subtract the seconds.

$$\begin{array}{r} 27°\ 35'\ 12" \\ -\ 13°\ 11'\ 42" \end{array}$$

$$\begin{array}{r} 27°\ 34'\ 72" \\ -\ 13°\ 11'\ 42" \\ \hline 30" \end{array}$$

Step 2: Subtract the minutes.

$$\begin{array}{r} 27°\ 34'\ 72" \\ -\ 13°\ 11'\ 42" \\ \hline 23'\ 30" \end{array}$$

Step 3: Subtract the degrees.

$$\begin{array}{r} 27°\ 34'\ 72" \\ -\ 13°\ 11'\ 42" \\ \hline 14°\ 23'\ 30" \end{array}$$

Subtract the following.

1) $\begin{array}{r} 34°\ 17'\ 45" \\ -\ 16°\ 5'\ 19" \end{array}$

2) $\begin{array}{r} 45°\ 18'\ 55" \\ -\ 22°\ 19'\ 26" \end{array}$

3) $\begin{array}{r} 1°\ 31'\ 15" \\ -\ \quad 30'\ 4" \end{array}$

4) $\begin{array}{r} 51°\ 26'\ 19" \\ -\ 18°\ 12'\ 45" \end{array}$

5) $\begin{array}{r} 39°\ 48'\ 15" \\ -\ 27°\ 32'\ 47" \end{array}$

6) $\begin{array}{r} 19°\ 3'\ 17" \\ -\ 4°\ 21'\ 12" \end{array}$

7) $\begin{array}{r} 0°\ 6'\ 8" \\ -\ 0°\ 5'\ 2" \end{array}$

8) $\begin{array}{r} 90°\ 14'\ 28" \\ -\ 17°\ 18'\ 36" \end{array}$

9) $\begin{array}{r} 42°\ 51'\ 18" \\ -\ 31°\ 59'\ 19" \end{array}$

10) $\begin{array}{r} 90°\ 0'\ 0" \\ -\ 21°\ 42'\ 39" \end{array}$

11) $\begin{array}{r} 72°\ 21'\ 17" \\ -\ 71°\ 59'\ 16" \end{array}$

12) $\begin{array}{r} 36°\ 24'\ 56" \\ -\ 18°\ 12'\ 28" \end{array}$

13) $\begin{array}{r} 56°\ 59'\ 1" \\ -\ 45°\ 1'\ 59" \end{array}$

14) $\begin{array}{r} 45°\ 0'\ 12" \\ -\ 22°\ 0'\ 13" \end{array}$

15) $\begin{array}{r} 27°\ 40'\ 0" \\ -\ 18°\ 51'\ 9" \end{array}$

16) $\begin{array}{r} 161°\ 14' \\ -\ 98°\ 12' \end{array}$

USING THE PYTHAGOREAN THEOREM AND TRIGONOMETRY

Both Pythagorean Theorem and trigonometry work with right-angle triangles. It is important to remember:

- All right-angle triangles have three sides: hypotenuse, opposite and adjacent. In the trades, the sides are often called travel, rise and run.
- One angle in a right-angle triangle is always 90°.
- The sum of the three angles in a triangle is always equal to 180°.
- The travel (hypotenuse) is always the longest side and is opposite the right angle (90°).
- The opposite and adjacent sides (rise and run) change depending on which angle you are working from.

Pythagorean Theorem

Workers in the construction trades commonly refer to the Pythagorean Theorem as the 3:4:5 Method. The right triangle with sides measuring 3 feet, 4 feet and 5 feet (or 3, 4, and 5 of any other unit) easily demonstrates the idea behind this theorem:

> If you multiply the length of each short side by itself, and add the two answers, the total is the length of the last side multiplied by itself.

Hint:

⌐ means a right angle.

$(3 \times 3) + (4 \times 4) = (5 \times 5)$.

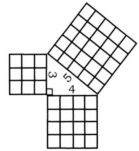

Hint:

"c" is always the hypotenuse.

Although the theorem is often called the 3:4:5 Method, the math works for right triangles of any shape or size. This method is used in the construction industry to lay out the perimeters of buildings, to ensure corners are square, and to calculate the length of rafters and stringers on stairs. Plumbers use this method to calculate lengths of pipes in piping systems. Crane operators and riggers use it to calculate the length of the boom and the length of slings used to lift loads.

Hint:

The perpendicular sides of a right triangle are also called the legs.

The basic formula is:

$$c^2 = a^2 + b^2$$
$$a^2 = c^2 - b^2$$
$$b^2 = c^2 - a^2$$

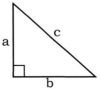

In the construction trades, the sides are often referred to as the travel, the rise and the run.

$$\text{travel}^2 = \text{rise}^2 + \text{run}^2$$
$$\text{rise}^2 = \text{travel}^2 - \text{run}^2$$
$$\text{run}^2 = \text{travel}^2 - \text{rise}^2$$

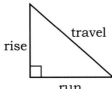

$$c^2 = a^2 + b^2$$
$$c^2 = 3^2 + 4^2$$
$$c^2 = 9 + 16$$
$$c^2 = 25$$
$$c = 5$$

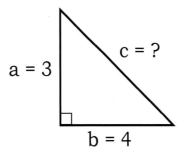

Sometimes you know the travel and need to calculate either the rise or the run.

$$b^2 = c^2 - a^2$$
$$b^2 = 5^2 - 3^2$$
$$b^2 = 25 - 9$$
$$b^2 = 16$$
$$b = \sqrt{16} = 4$$

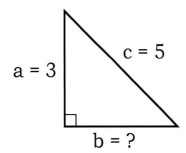

To calculate the rise use:

$$a^2 = c^2 - b^2$$
$$a^2 = 5^2 - 4^2$$
$$a^2 = 25 - 16$$
$$a^2 = 9$$
$$a = \sqrt{9} = 3$$

Calculate the length of the missing side in the following right angle triangles. Round off answers to two decimal places.

1) rise = 1.8 m
    run = 2.7 m

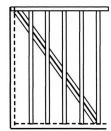

2) rise = 7' - 0"
    run = 11' - 0"

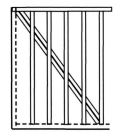

3) rise = 2.5 m
    travel = 15.3 m

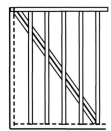

4) run = 16' - 0"
    travel = 20'

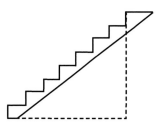

5) travel = 62 267 mm
    total run = 2 900 mm

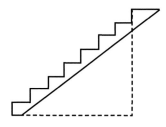

6) total rise = 1 000 mm
    total run = 2 455 mm

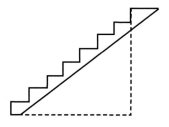

7) run = 4 236 mm
    total rise = 1 955 mm
    overhang = 850 mm

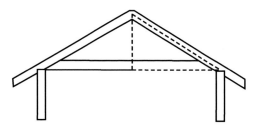

8) run = 1 829 mm
    total rise = 1 355 mm
    overhang = 305 mm

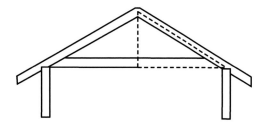

9) run = 2 400 mm
    total rise = 1 500 mm
    overhang = 350 mm

10) run = 6 875 mm
    total rise = 3 658 mm
    overhang = 875 mm

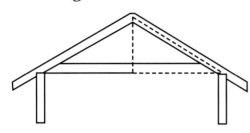

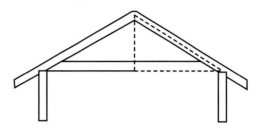

TRIGONOMETRY

You must know at least two values in order to solve angles or lengths of a right angle triangle. You can solve a right-angle triangle if you know

- ❏ the length of two of the sides
- ❏ one of the angles and the length of one of the sides

Remember: the hypotenuse (travel) is always the longest side and is always opposite the right angle.

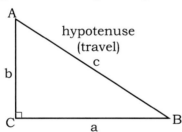

The opposite and adjacent sides of a right triangle change depending on which angle is used as the reference point. It is important to learn how to identify the sides in a right triangle because it will make trigonometry easier to understand.

If ∠A is the reference point:

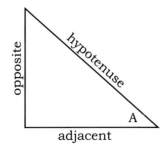

If ∠B is the reference point:

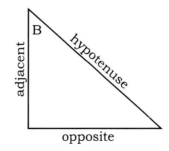

RIGHT-ANGLE TRIANGLES

Identify opposite and adjacent in the right angle triangles below using the identified angle as the reference point.

1)
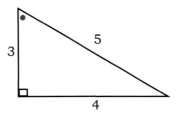

2)
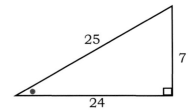

3)
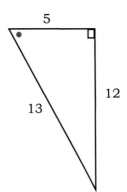

4)
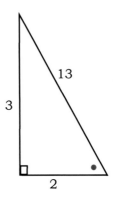

5)
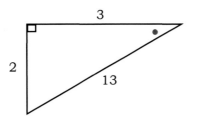

6)
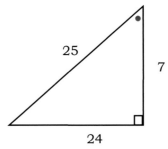

7)
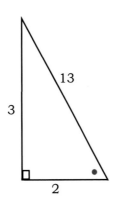

8)
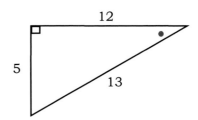

9)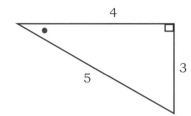

10)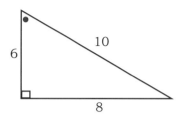

TRIGONOMETRIC RATIOS

Ratio describes the proportional relationship between two things. The three sides of a right-angle triangle hypotenuse, opposite and adjacent-have a fixed relationship with each other. This means that as one of the three sides increases or decreases in length, the other two sides increase or decrease proportionately.

There are three basic trigonometric ratios: sine, cosine and tangent.

1. The sine of an angle is the ratio of the length of the opposite side to the length of the hypotenuse. The abbreviation of sine is "sin".

$$\sin = \frac{\text{opposite side}}{\text{hypotenuse}}$$

2. The cosine of an angle is the ratio of the length of the adjacent side to the length of the hypotenuse. The abbreviation of cosine is "cos".

$$\cos = \frac{\text{adjacent side}}{\text{hypotenuse}}$$

3. The tangent of an angle is the ratio of the length of the opposite side to the length of the adjacent side. The abbreviation of tangent is "tan".

$$\tan = \frac{\text{opposite side}}{\text{adjacent side}}$$

One way to remember these three trigonometric functions is: SOHCAHTOA.

SOH
$$s = \frac{o}{h}$$

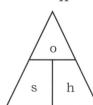

CAH
$$c = \frac{a}{h}$$

TOA
$$t = \frac{o}{a}$$

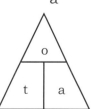

Using the triangles makes it easier to know when to multiply or divide.

Example:

Cover up the value you are asked to calculate with your finger.

Note:

θ is the Greek letter theta. It is used to represent the angle. sin θ means the sine of angle theta.

♦   If the two that remain are next to each other, you multiply them
opposite = sin θ × hypotenuse

♦   If you know one of the bottom corners, then divide the top corner by the other bottom corner.

sin θ = opposite ÷ hypotenuse
hypotenuse = opposite ÷ sin θ

Sine, cosine and tangent each have a reciprocal ratio: secant, cosecant and cotangent. These three trigonometric functions are not explained in this chapter because they are not commonly used by trades workers.

Calculating the Length of a Side

If you know an angle and the length of one of the sides, you can calculate the length of one of the other sides.

Example 1:

Calculate the length of the hypotenuse (travel).

Step 1:   Draw a diagram and label it.

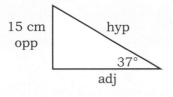

Label the diagram with the known information. Label the sides hypotenuse, opposite and adjacent.

Step 2:   Write the trig ratio needed to solve the problem. Calculate the length of the hypotenuse. Use sin because you know the length of the side opposite to the 37° angle.

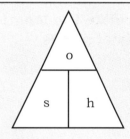

$$\text{hypotenuse} = \frac{\text{opposite}}{\sin}$$

Step 3:   Calculate the length of the side.

$$\text{hypotenuse} = \frac{\text{opposite}}{\sin} = \frac{15 \text{ cm}}{\sin 37°} = 24.92 \text{ cm}$$

Note: Some calculators require the degrees to be entered before pressing the sin, cos or tan button. Other calculators require the sin, cos or tan button to be pressed before entering the degrees.

Example 2:

Calculate the length of the adjacent side.

Step 1:   Draw a diagram and label it.

Label the diagram with the known information. Label the sides hypotenuse, opposite and adjacent.

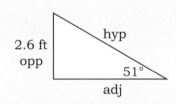

Step 2:   Write the trig ratio needed to solve the problem. Calculate the length of the adjacent side. Use tan because you know the length of the side opposite to the 51° angle.

$$\text{adjacent} = \frac{\text{opposite}}{\tan}$$

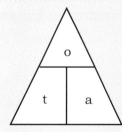

Step 3:   Calculate the length of the side.

$$\text{adjacent} = \frac{\text{opposite}}{\tan} = \frac{2.6 \text{ ft}}{\tan 51°} = 2.11 \text{ ft}$$

Hint:

Measurements must be in the same unit of measurement. Label the hypotenuse, opposite and adjacent sides.

Calculate the length of the indicated side. Round off answers to two decimal places.

Hint

Refer to the chapter on Fractions for converting inches to decimals of a foot.

1)   Calculate the length of the hypotenuse.

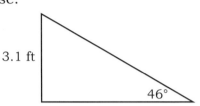

2)   Calculate the length of the hypotenuse.

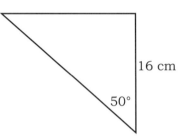

3)   Calculate the length of the adjacent.

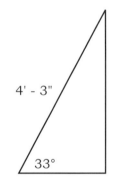

4)   Calculate the length of the opposite.

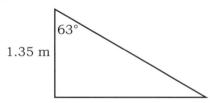

5)   Calculate the length of the adjacent.

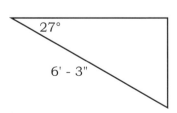

6) Calculate the length of the hypotenuse.

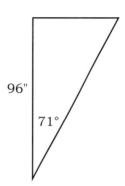

7) Calculate the length of the opposite.

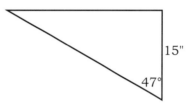

8) Calculate the length of the opposite.

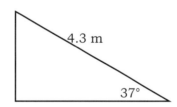

9) Calculate the length of the hypotenuse.

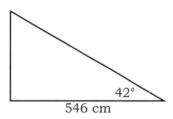

10) Calculate the length of the adjacent.

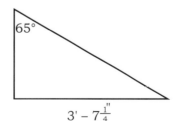

Calculating the Size of an Angle

If you know the length of two of the sides, you can calculate an angle using trigonometry.

Example 1:

Calculate the size of the angle indicated in the diagram.

Step 1:   Draw a diagram and label it.

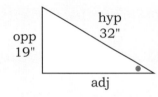

Label the diagram with the known information. Label the sides hypotenuse, opposite and adjacent.

Step 2:   Write the trig ratio needed to solve the problem. Calculate the size of the angle marked with a dot.

Use sin because you know the length of the side opposite the angle that you are asked to solve and the length of the hypotenuse.

$$\sin = \frac{\text{opposite}}{\text{hypotenuse}}$$

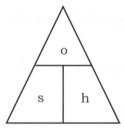

Step 3:   Calculate the angle.

$$\sin = \frac{\text{opposite}}{\text{hypotenuse}} = \frac{19}{32} = 0.59375$$

Press 2nd function. Press sin.

$$= 36.42°$$

Example 2:

Calculate the size of the angle indicated in the diagram.

Step 1:   Draw a diagram and label it.

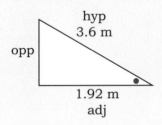

Label the diagram with the known information.
Label the sides hypotenuse, opposite and adjacent.

Step 2:   Write the trig ratio needed to solve the problem.

$$\cos = \frac{\text{adjacent}}{\text{hypotenuse}}$$

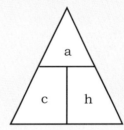

Calculate the size of the angle marked with a dot.

Use cos because you know the length of the side adjacent to the angle that you are asked to solve and the length of the hypotenuse.

Step 3:   Calculate the angle.

$$\cos = \frac{\text{adjacent}}{\text{hypotenuse}} = \frac{1.92 \text{ m}}{3.6 \text{ m}} = 0.533333333$$

Press 2nd function. Press cos.

$$= 57.77°$$

RIGHT-ANGLE TRIANGLES

Calculate the size of the angle indicated. Round off answers to two decimal places.

Hint:

Measurements must be in the same unit of measurement.

1)

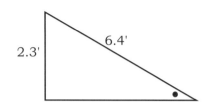

2)

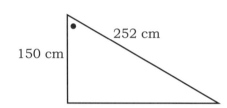

3)

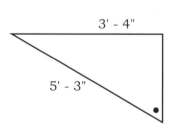

4)

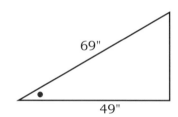

5)

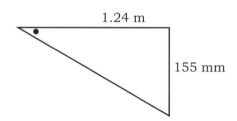

6)

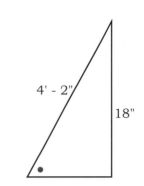

7)

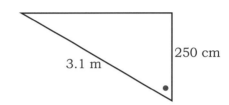

8)

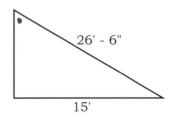

9)

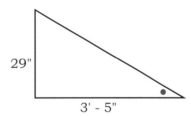

10)

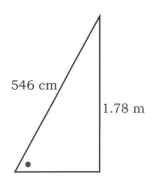

WORKING WITH MULTI-SIDED SHAPES

Sometimes the shape you are working with does not seem to have any right-angle triangles. You may need to draw on other information to solve the problem.

Example:
Calculate angle A and angle B, side b and side c.

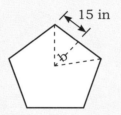

At first glance, it looks as if there is not enough information to solve the triangle because two pieces of information are needed to use trigonometry: the length of two of the sides, or the length of one side and the size of one of the angles. However, there is enough information to solve the triangle.

The shape has five equal sides and is called a pentagon.

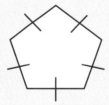

Because the sides are equal, five equal triangles are formed when lines are drawn from each of the five points to the centre of the pentagon.

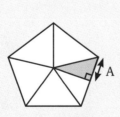

Pentagon

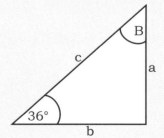

Divide each triangle in half by drawing a perpendicular line from the centre point to the base of the triangle. Now there are 10 equal-sized right-angle triangles.

- Calculate angle A.

There are 360° in one full turn – all the way around the centre point of the pentagon. Divide 360° by 10. The answer is the size of angle A.

angle A = 360° ÷ 10 = 36°

side a = 15 in

- Calculate angle B.

90° − 36° = 54°

- Calculate side b.

Use trigonometry. Label the sides opposite, adjacent and hypotenuse.

angle A = 36°

side a = 15 in

$$\text{adjacent} = \frac{\text{opposite}}{\tan} = \frac{15 \text{ in}}{\tan 36°} = \frac{15 \text{ in}}{.0726542528} = 20.65 \text{ in}$$

side b = 20.65 in

- Calculate side c.

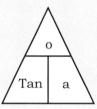

Use either trig or Pythagorean Theorem.

Using Trigonometry	Using Pythagorean Theorem
Note: There are several ways to calculate side C using trig depending on which angle is used and which trig function.	$a^2 + b^2 = c^2$
	$15^2 + 20.65^2 = c^2$
	$225 + 426.42 = c^2$
$\text{hypotenuse} = \frac{\text{opposite}}{\sin} = \frac{15 \text{ in}}{\sin 36°} = \frac{15 \text{ in}}{0.5878} = 25.52 \text{ in}$	$\sqrt{651.42} = c$
	$25.52 \text{ in} = c$

Solve the triangles in the following shapes.

1. angle A =

   angle B =

   side a =

   side b = 20 ft

   side c =

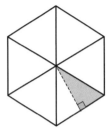

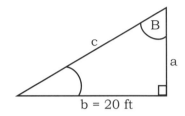

2. angle A =

   angle B =

   side a =

   side b =

   side c = 24 ft

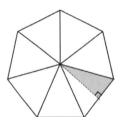

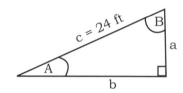

Hint:

Draw a diagram and label it with the known information.

3. angle A =

   angle B =

   side a = 8 m

   side b =

   side c =

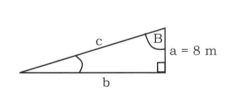

PRACTICE

1) A foreman wants to know if two walls are perpendicular (90°) to each other. One wall is 5 ft long and the other wall is 12 ft long. What should the diagonal distance from corner to corner measure?

$$C = \sqrt{5^2 + 12^2}$$
$$= \sqrt{25 + 144}$$
$$= \sqrt{169}$$
$$= 13'$$

2) A carpenter wants to brace the top of an eight-foot wall to a peg 15' from the base of the wall. Calculate the length of the brace.

3) A brace 6.5 m long is used to stabilize a wall. If the brace is attached to the wall at a point 6 m up the wall, how far from the base must it be secured?

4) Calculate the diagonal length of the staircase below.

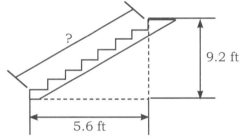

5) Calculate the length of the rafter needed in the diagram below. The overhang is 3 ft long.

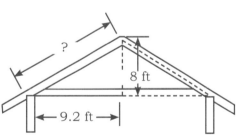

6) Look at the diagram of the building lot below. The diagonal line measures 71.1 ft and the width is 46.6 ft. Calculate the length of the building lot.

$a = \sqrt{71.1^2 - 46.6^2}$

$a = \sqrt{5055.21 - 2171.56}$

$a = \sqrt{2883.65}$

$= 53.69962756'$

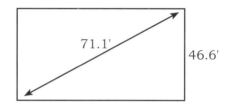

71.1'

46.6'

7) A ladder is leaning against a 15 ft wall at a 75° angle. The ladder must extend 3 ft over the wall according to Health and Safety Regulations. Calculate the length of ladder needed.

8) Calculate the length of the rafter in the diagram below.

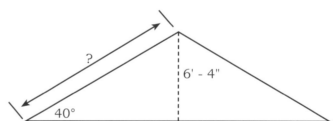

?

6' - 4"

40°

9) Calculate the length of the beams labelled x in the bridge truss shown below. The marked angle is 25°.

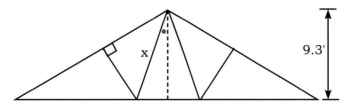

9.3'

Hint:

Refer to Working with Multi-sided Shapes for help.

10) Eight holes are drilled evenly spaced in a piece of plywood with a 3 ft radius. Calculate the distance between the holes centre-to-centre.

3'

RIGHT-ANGLE TRIANGLES

ANSWER KEY

WHOLE NUMBERS

Page 2, **Place Value**

1) 3 thousands, 6 ones

2) 0 ten thousands, 3 hundreds

3) 7 thousands, 6 tens

4) 2 hundred thousands, 5 tens

Page 4, **Rounding Whole Numbers**

1)	10	2)	160	3)	290	4)	2 840
5)	100	6)	600	7)	8 300	8)	10 600
9)	1 000	10)	4 000	11)	28 000	12)	52 000

Page 5, **Adding Whole Numbers**

1)	106	2)	184	3)	141	4)	101
5)	920	6)	1 000	7)	110	8)	131
9)	17	10)	21	11)	174	12)	121

Page 7, **Subtracting Whole Numbers**

1)	44	2)	52	3)	89	4)	17
5)	89	6)	145	7)	88	8)	478
9)	102	10)	419	11)	69	12)	358

Page 10, **Multiplying Whole Numbers**

1)	882	2)	169	3)	5 041	4)	33 744
5)	81 328	6)	66 096	7)	419 405	8)	71 100

ng **Whole Numbers**

	2) 21	3) 43	4) 32
	6) 31	7) 28	8) 32
9) 1 005	10) 109	11) 201	12) 105
13) 17 R11	14) 23 R4	15) 37 R11	16) 41 R38

Page 15, **Order of Operations**

1) $9 + 8 \times 3 = 9 + 24 = 33$

2) $6 \times 8 + 6 = 48 + 6 = 54$

3) $13 \times 2 - 2 = 26 - 2 = 24$

4) $20 \times 10 \div 5 = 20 \times 2 = 40$

5) $36 \div (8 - 2) = 36 \div 6 = 6$

6) $(20 - 11) \div (6 \div 2) = 9 \div 3 = 3$

7) $20 \div (2 \times 5) = 20 \div 10 = 2$

8) $(35 \div 7) - (8 \div 4) = 5 - 2 = 3$

9) $5^2 - 6 \div 2 = 25 - 6 \div 2 = 25 - 3 = 22$

10) $9 \times 5 + (7 - 2) - 4^2 = 9 \times 5 + 5 - 4^2 = 9 \times 5 + 5 - 16 = 45 + 5 - 16 = 50 - 16 = 34$

Page 16, **Practice**

1) 4 254 board feet

2) 594 hours

3) $3 352

4) 963 sq. feet

5) $513

6) 694 square feet

7) 2 945 mm

8) $97 206

9) 296 feet

10) 15 860 mm

11) 238 board feet

12) 1 164 snap ties

13) 74 nails

14) a) 5 pieces   b) 1 foot

15) a) 10 pieces   b) 6 inches

16) a) 142 headers   b) 6 nails left over

17) a) 112 cubic feet   b) 368 feet

18) 144 minutes

19) 56 lineal feet

20) 96 hours

ANSWER KEY

DECIMALS

Page 22, **Rounding Decimals.**

To the nearest tenth.

1) 5.4   2) 2.4   3) 15.4   4) 238.0

5) 17.9   6) 1.9   7) 456.7   8) 322.2

To the nearest hundredth.

1) 91.44   2) 26.38   3) 2.06   4) 1.01

5) 12.04   6) 18.03   7) 5.04   8) 0.01

To the nearest thousandth.

1) 1.034   2) 10.512   3) 19.999   4) 32.766

5) 155.333   6) 43.883   7) 26.747   8) 717.230

Page 23, **Converting Fractions to Decimals.**

1) 0.625   2) 0.250   3) 0.688   4) 0.375

5) 0.333   6) 0.429   7) 0.500   8) 0.559

Page 24, **Converting Decimals to Fractions.**

1) $\frac{3}{10}$ 2) $\frac{7}{10}$ 3) $\frac{4}{100} = \frac{1}{25}$ 4) $\frac{39}{100}$

5) $\frac{90}{100} = \frac{9}{10}$ 6) $\frac{4}{1000} = \frac{1}{250}$ 7) $\frac{84}{1000} = \frac{21}{250}$ 8) $\frac{91}{1000}$

9) $\frac{137}{1000}$ 10) $\frac{871}{1000}$ 11) $\frac{442}{1000} = \frac{221}{500}$ 12) $\frac{1}{10\,000}$

13) $\frac{4}{10} = 6\frac{2}{5}$ 14) $3\frac{14}{100} = 3\frac{7}{50}$ 15) $7\frac{2}{100} = 7\frac{1}{50}$

16) $40\frac{1}{100}$ 17) $\frac{15}{100} = \frac{3}{20}$ 18) $9\frac{8}{100} = 9\frac{2}{25}$

19) $31\frac{812}{1000} = 31\frac{203}{250}$ 20) $1\frac{4}{1000} = 1\frac{1}{250}$ 21) $328\frac{76}{100} = 328\frac{19}{25}$

22) $408\frac{2}{10} = 408\frac{1}{5}$ 23) $6\frac{222}{1000} = 6\frac{111}{500}$ 24) $81\frac{5}{100} = 81\frac{1}{20}$

Page 25, **Adding Decimals**

1) 33.101	2) 92.22	3) 15.6347	4) 22.7167
5) 9.961 m	6) 32.287 ft	7) 90.0074	8) 562.9924

Page 26, **Subtracting Decimals**

1) 2.44	2) 1.2	3) 11.22	4) 0.98
5) 2.219	6) 1.74	7) 1.033	8) 699.999

Page 27, **Multiplying Decimals**

1) 10.8	2) 0.8	3) 7.2	4) 2.73
5) 2.8325	6) 1.853	7) 0.03006	8) 0.0482

Page 30, **Dividing Decimals**

1) 28.4	2) 3.27	3) 0.003	4) 63.7
5) 0.577	6) 3.274	7) 0.2625	8) 0.1874
9) 7	10) 4	11) 21	12) 0.8
13) 0.12	14) 25.5	15) 30.3	16) 23.957
17) 42 000	18) 70	19) 700	20) 18

DECIMALS OF A FOOT

Page 33, **Decimals of a Foot.**

1) .06'	2) .14'	3) .51'	4) 1.0'
5) .70'	6) .50'	7) .66'	8) .31'
9) .10'	10) .80'		

Page 35, **Decimals of a Foot.**

1) 9.79'	2) 3.28'	3) 6.93'	4) 1.05'
5) 25.4'	6) 16.48'	7) 12.10'	8) 1.52'

Page 35, **Decimals of a Foot.**

1) $7' - 3\frac{3}{8}''$	2) $6' - 6\frac{3}{4}''$	3) $26' - 7\frac{1}{4}''$	4) $2' - 11\frac{3}{8}''$
5) $42' - 2\frac{3}{4}''$	6) $12' - 6\frac{1}{8}''$	7) $13' - 1\frac{7}{8}''$	8) $0' - 9\frac{5}{8}''$

Page 36, **Practice**

1) $57.41   2) 1 097.57 board feet 3) 0.456 m 4) $25.78

5) 0.0038 m   6) $16.26   7) 26.438 cm   8) 1.219 m

9 a) 64.077 m³ = 64.08 m³   b) 8.887 m³ = 8.89 m³

10) 33.5"   11) 2.382 m   12) 0.191 m

13 a) $15.56   b) $124.48   14) 9.938 m   15) 0.786 m³

16) 0.239 m   17) $40.17   18) 3.965 m

19 a) $3.94   b) $3.28   c) $64.03   20) $630.75

ANSWER KEY

FRACTIONS

Page 43, **Defining Fractions**

1) proper fraction   2) mixed number   3) improper fraction

4) whole number   5) proper fraction   6) mixed number

7) proper fraction   8) improper fraction   9) improper fraction

10) whole number   11) proper fraction   12) proper fraction

13) mixed number   14) improper fraction   15) improper fraction

16) mixed number

Page 43, **Writing Fractions**

1) $\frac{1}{2}$ 2) $\frac{1}{3}$ 3) $\frac{3}{8}$ 4) $\frac{7}{8}$

5) $\frac{1}{3}$ 6) $\frac{3}{4}$ 7) $\frac{3}{16}$ 8) $\frac{10}{16}$

Page 44, **Changing Improper Fractions to Mixed Numbers**

1) 2   2) $1\frac{2}{8} = 1\frac{1}{4}$ 3) 2   4) 3

5) $1\frac{1}{3}$ 6) $2\frac{2}{4} = 2\frac{1}{2}$ 7) $1\frac{1}{2}$ 8) $2\frac{1}{2}$

9) $1\frac{5}{8}$ 10) 7   11) $1\frac{3}{4}$ 12) 3

13) $1\frac{1}{4}$ 14) $3\frac{1}{2}$ 15) $1\frac{1}{16}$ 16) $1\frac{5}{16}$

Page 45, **Changing Mixed Numbers to Improper Fractions**

1) $\frac{3}{2}$ 2) $\frac{4}{3}$ 3) $\frac{9}{4}$ 4) $\frac{25}{8}$

5) $\frac{4}{1}$ 6) $\frac{15}{2}$ 7) $\frac{15}{4}$ 8) $\frac{99}{16}$

9) $\frac{11}{1}$ 10) $\frac{155}{16}$ 11) $\frac{37}{8}$ 12) $\frac{27}{8}$

13) $\frac{17}{8}$ 14) $\frac{28}{3}$ 15) $\frac{21}{1}$ 16) $\frac{55}{8}$

Page 46, **Common Denominators**

1) $\frac{3}{4} = \frac{6}{8}$

2) $\frac{1}{2} = \frac{4}{8}$

3) $\frac{1}{3} = \frac{2}{6}$

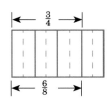

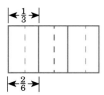

4) $\frac{1}{4} = \frac{2}{8}$

5) $\frac{3}{4} = \frac{12}{16}$

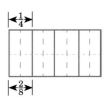

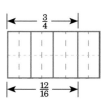

Page 47, **Common Denominators**

1) The LCD is 4, $\frac{1}{2} = \frac{2}{4}$

2) The LCD is 8, $\frac{1}{4} = \frac{2}{8}$

3) The LCD is 12, $\frac{1}{3} = \frac{4}{12}$

4) The LCD is 16, $\frac{3}{8} = \frac{6}{16}$

5) The LCD is 10, $\frac{1}{5} = \frac{2}{10}$, $\frac{1}{2} = \frac{5}{10}$

6) The LCD is 8, $\frac{3}{4} = \frac{6}{8}$

7) The LCD is 6, $\frac{1}{2} = \frac{3}{6}$, $\frac{1}{3} = \frac{2}{6}$

8) The LCD is 24, $\frac{1}{12} = \frac{2}{24}$, $\frac{1}{8} = \frac{3}{24}$

9) The LCD is 12, $\frac{2}{3} = \frac{8}{12}$, $\frac{3}{4} = \frac{9}{12}$

10) The LCD is 16, $\frac{5}{8} = \frac{10}{16}$

11) The LCD is 20, $\frac{3}{4} = \frac{15}{20}$, $\frac{2}{5} = \frac{8}{20}$

12) The LCD is 20, $\frac{3}{5} = \frac{15}{25}$

13) The LCD is 8, $\frac{1}{2} = \frac{4}{8}$

14) The LCD is 16, $\frac{3}{4} = \frac{12}{16}$

15) The LCD is 24, $\frac{2}{6} = \frac{8}{24}$, $\frac{3}{8} = \frac{9}{24}$

16) The LCD is 16, $\frac{3}{8} = \frac{6}{16}$

Page 48, **Multiplying Fractions**

1) $\frac{1}{12}$

2) $\frac{2}{15}$

3) $\frac{2}{12} = \frac{1}{6}$

4) $\frac{7}{40}$

5) $\frac{2}{4} = \frac{1}{2}$

6) $\frac{5}{3} = 1\frac{2}{3}$

7) $\frac{9}{2} = 4\frac{1}{2}$

8) $\frac{8}{3} = 2\frac{2}{3}$

9) $\frac{20}{3} = 6\frac{2}{3}$

10) $\frac{42}{5} = 8\frac{2}{5}$

11) $\frac{74}{4} = 18\frac{2}{4} = 18\frac{1}{2}$

12) $\frac{14}{4} = 3\frac{2}{4} = 3\frac{1}{2}$

13) $\frac{90}{24} = 3\frac{18}{24} = 3\frac{3}{4}$

14) $\frac{169}{32} = 5\frac{9}{32}$

15) $\frac{45}{32} = 1\frac{13}{32}$　　　　16) $\frac{65}{6} = 10\frac{5}{6}$　　　17) $\frac{100}{12} = 8\frac{4}{12} = 8\frac{1}{3}$

18) $\frac{21}{4} = 5\frac{1}{4}$　　　　19) $\frac{969}{32} = 30\frac{9}{32}$　　20) $\frac{255}{32} = 7\frac{31}{32}$

Page 49, Inverting Fractions

1) $\frac{8}{7}$　　　　2) $\frac{4}{3}$　　　　3) $\frac{1}{2}$　　　　4) $\frac{3}{2}$

5) $\frac{2}{9}$　　　　6) $\frac{4}{7}$　　　　7) $\frac{8}{3}$　　　　8) $\frac{8}{5}$

9) $\frac{2}{3}$　　　　10) $\frac{16}{35}$　　　11) $\frac{8}{53}$　　　12) $\frac{4}{15}$

13) $\frac{4}{21}$　　　14) $\frac{16}{137}$　　15) $\frac{4}{19}$　　　16) $\frac{2}{15}$

Page 51, Dividing Fractions

1) $\frac{1}{3} \times \frac{2}{1} = \frac{2}{3}$　　2) $\frac{2}{5} \times \frac{2}{1} = \frac{4}{5}$　　3) $\frac{1}{4} \times \frac{3}{1} = \frac{3}{4}$　　4) $\frac{2}{3} \times \frac{4}{3} = \frac{8}{9}$

5) $\frac{3}{7} \times \frac{9}{4} = \frac{27}{28}$　　6) $\frac{2}{11} \times \frac{8}{5} = \frac{16}{55}$　　7) $\frac{1}{3} \times \frac{3}{2} = \frac{3}{6} = \frac{1}{2}$　　8) $\frac{5}{16} \times \frac{3}{2} = \frac{15}{32}$

9) $\frac{15}{2} \div \frac{1}{3} = \frac{15}{2} \times \frac{3}{1} = \frac{45}{2} = 22\frac{1}{2}$　　10) $\frac{6}{1} \times \frac{3}{2} = \frac{18}{2} = 9$

11) $\frac{3}{1} \times \frac{4}{7} = \frac{12}{7} = 1\frac{5}{7}$　　　　12) $\frac{2}{3} \times \frac{1}{4} = \frac{2}{12} = \frac{1}{6}$

13) $\frac{1}{16} \div \frac{9}{8} = \frac{1}{16} \times \frac{8}{9} = \frac{8}{144} = \frac{1}{18}$　　14) $\frac{8}{3} \div \frac{4}{1} = \frac{8}{3} \times \frac{1}{4} = \frac{8}{12} = \frac{2}{3}$

15) $\frac{6}{5} \div \frac{3}{1} = \frac{6}{5} \times \frac{1}{3} = \frac{6}{15} = \frac{2}{5}$　　16) $\frac{19}{8} \div \frac{1}{1} = \frac{19}{8} \times \frac{1}{1} = 2\frac{3}{8}$

17) $\frac{15}{2} \div \frac{7}{2} = \frac{15}{2} \times \frac{2}{7} = \frac{30}{14} = 2\frac{2}{14} = 2\frac{1}{7}$　18) $\frac{5}{4} \div \frac{19}{8} = \frac{5}{4} \times \frac{8}{19} = \frac{40}{76} = \frac{10}{19}$

19) $\frac{9}{8} \div \frac{8}{3} = \frac{9}{8} \times \frac{3}{8} = \frac{27}{64}$　　　20) $\frac{21}{8} \div \frac{19}{8} = \frac{21}{8} \times \frac{8}{19} = \frac{168}{152} = 1\frac{16}{152} = 1\frac{2}{19}$

Page 53, Adding Fractions

1) $\frac{3}{4}$　　　　2) $\frac{4}{4} = 1$　　　3) $\frac{4}{8} = \frac{1}{2}$　　4) $\frac{12}{8} = 1\frac{4}{8} = 1\frac{1}{2}$

5) $\frac{2}{4} + \frac{1}{4} = \frac{3}{4}$　　6) $\frac{3}{6} + \frac{2}{6} = \frac{5}{6}$　　7) $\frac{5}{6}$　　　8) $\frac{2}{8} + \frac{3}{8} = \frac{9}{8} = \frac{5}{8}$

9) $\frac{10}{16} + \frac{13}{16} = \frac{23}{16} = 1\frac{7}{16}$　　　10) $\frac{10}{12} + \frac{3}{12} = \frac{13}{12} = 1\frac{1}{12}$

11) $\frac{2}{8} + \frac{7}{8} = \frac{9}{8} = 1\frac{1}{8}$　　　　12) $\frac{5}{16} + \frac{12}{16} = \frac{17}{16} = 1\frac{1}{16}$

13) $13\frac{2}{8} = 13\frac{1}{4}$　　　　14) $6\frac{2}{16} + 4\frac{3}{16} = 10\frac{5}{16}$

15) $2\frac{2}{4} + 1\frac{1}{4} = 3\frac{3}{4}$

16) $5\frac{2}{6} + 7\frac{1}{6} = 12\frac{3}{6} = 12\frac{1}{2}$

17) $15\frac{6}{8} = 15\frac{3}{4}$

18) $2\frac{1}{16} + 3\frac{2}{16} + 7\frac{7}{16} = 12\frac{10}{16} = 12\frac{5}{8}$

19) $2\frac{4}{16} + 4\frac{8}{16} + 5\frac{7}{16} = 11\frac{19}{16} = 12\frac{3}{16}$

20) $3\frac{2}{8} + 9\frac{3}{8} + 1\frac{6}{8} = 13\frac{11}{8} = 14\frac{3}{8}$

Page 56, Subtracting Fractions

1) $\frac{2}{4} = \frac{1}{2}$

2) $\frac{2}{8} = \frac{1}{4}$

3) $\frac{8}{16} = \frac{1}{2}$

4) $\frac{4}{8} = \frac{1}{2}$

5) $\frac{3}{4} - \frac{2}{4} = \frac{1}{4}$

6) $\frac{3}{6} - \frac{2}{6} = \frac{1}{6}$

7) $\frac{3}{8} - \frac{2}{8} = \frac{1}{8}$

8) $\frac{11}{16} - \frac{6}{16} = \frac{5}{16}$

9) $2\frac{5}{8}$

10) $5\frac{10}{16} - 1\frac{5}{16} = 4\frac{5}{16}$

11) $3\frac{4}{6} - 1\frac{3}{6} = 2\frac{1}{6}$

12) $4\frac{3}{8} - 1\frac{2}{8} = 3\frac{1}{8}$

13) $2\frac{5}{4} - 1\frac{3}{4} = 1\frac{2}{4} = 1\frac{1}{2}$

14) $11\frac{11}{8} - 5\frac{5}{8} = 6\frac{6}{8} = 6\frac{3}{4}$

15) $2\frac{1}{4} - 1\frac{2}{4} = 1\frac{5}{4} - 1\frac{2}{4} = \frac{3}{4}$

16) $2\frac{2}{4} - \frac{3}{4} = 1\frac{6}{4} - \frac{3}{4} = 1\frac{3}{4}$

17) $4\frac{4}{4} - 1\frac{3}{4} = 3\frac{1}{4}$

18) $\frac{8}{8} - \frac{5}{8} = \frac{3}{8}$

19) $6\frac{16}{16} - \frac{15}{16} = 6\frac{1}{16}$

20) $5\frac{8}{8} - 4\frac{1}{8} = 1\frac{7}{8}$

21) $7\frac{5}{8} - 2\frac{6}{8} = 6\frac{13}{8} - 2\frac{6}{8} = 4\frac{7}{8}$

22) $15\frac{4}{16} - 13\frac{5}{16} = 14\frac{20}{16} - 13\frac{5}{16} = 1\frac{15}{16}$

23) $2\frac{2}{10} - 1\frac{1}{10} = 1\frac{1}{10}$

24) $3\frac{5}{8} - 1\frac{6}{8} = 2\frac{13}{8} - 1\frac{6}{8} = 1\frac{7}{8}$

Page 57, Practice

1) $\frac{1}{2} \times \frac{1}{4} = \frac{1}{8}$

2) $\frac{1}{4} \times \frac{1}{3} = \frac{1}{12}$

3) $3\frac{1}{4} + 6\frac{1}{8} + 2\frac{5}{16} = 3\frac{4}{16} + 6\frac{2}{16} + 2\frac{5}{16} = 11\frac{11}{16}''$

4) $4\frac{1}{4} \times 8 = \frac{17}{4} \times \frac{8}{1} = \frac{136}{4} = 34'$

5) $7\frac{1}{2} \div 1\frac{1}{2} = \frac{15}{2} \div \frac{3}{2} = \frac{15}{2} \times \frac{2}{3} = \frac{30}{6} = 5$ pieces

6) $\frac{5}{8} + 9\frac{1}{4} + 11\frac{3}{8} = \frac{5}{8} + 9\frac{2}{8} + 11\frac{3}{8} = 20\frac{10}{8} = 21\frac{2}{8} = 21\frac{1}{4}''$

7) $A = 7\frac{3}{4} + 2\frac{3}{8} = 7\frac{6}{8} + 2\frac{3}{8} = 9\frac{9}{8} = 10\frac{1}{8}''$

8) $B = 7\frac{1}{2} + 1\frac{7}{8} = 7\frac{4}{8} + 1\frac{7}{8} = 8\frac{11}{8} = 9\frac{3}{8}''$

9) $C = 5\frac{1}{2} + 1\frac{1}{2} = 6\frac{2}{2} = 7''$

10) $D = A + 6\frac{1}{4} = 10\frac{1}{8} + 6\frac{1}{4} = 10\frac{1}{8} + 6\frac{2}{8} = 16\frac{3}{8}''$

11) $A = 16'\ 3'' - (8' + 3'\ \frac{7}{8}\ '')$
$= 16'\ 3'' - 11'\ \frac{7}{8}\ '' = 5'\ 2\frac{1}{8}\ ''$

12) $13 \times 7\frac{3}{8} = \frac{13}{1} \times \frac{59}{8} = \frac{767}{8} = 95\frac{7}{8}'' = 7' - 11\frac{7}{8}''$

13a) $15 \div \frac{5}{8} = \frac{15}{1} \div \frac{5}{8} = \frac{15}{1} \times \frac{8}{5} = \frac{120}{5} = 24$ sheets

b) $8\frac{1}{8} \div \frac{5}{8} = \frac{65}{8} \div \frac{5}{8} = \frac{65}{8} \times \frac{8}{5} = \frac{520}{40} = 13$ sheets

14) $B = 8' + 10'\ 6\frac{3}{4}\ '' + 8' + 3'\ \frac{7}{8}\ '' + 6'$
$= 35'\ 6\frac{13}{8}\ '' = 35'\ 7\frac{5}{8}\ ''$

15) kerf $= \frac{1}{8} \times \frac{3}{1} = \frac{3}{8}''$

length of board =
$3\frac{3}{8} + 2\frac{7}{16} + 4\frac{1}{2} + 1\frac{1}{4} + \frac{3}{8} = 3\frac{6}{16} + 2\frac{7}{16} + 4\frac{8}{16} + 1\frac{4}{16} + \frac{6}{16} = 10\frac{31}{16} = 11\frac{15}{16}''$

16) $103\frac{3}{16} + 10\frac{1}{4} + 12\frac{3}{4} = 103\frac{3}{16} + 10\frac{4}{16} + 12\frac{12}{16} = 125\frac{19}{16} = 126\frac{3}{16}''$

17) $7 \times \frac{3}{8} = \frac{21}{8} = 2\frac{5}{8}''$

18) $4' \times 12 = 48''$
$(48 + 10) \div 8 = 58 \div 8 = 7\frac{2}{8} = 7\frac{1}{4}''$

19) $7\frac{3}{8} \div \frac{1}{8} = \frac{59}{8} \times \frac{8}{1} = \frac{472}{8} = 59'$

20) $117 \div 2\frac{1}{3} = \frac{117}{1} \div \frac{7}{3} = \frac{117}{1} \times \frac{3}{7} = \frac{351}{7} = 50\frac{1}{7} = 51$ strips

21) $5\frac{3}{8} + 2\frac{1}{16} + 3\frac{5}{8} = 5\frac{6}{16} + 2\frac{1}{16} + 3\frac{10}{16} = 10\frac{17}{16} = 11\frac{1}{16}''$

22) $9\frac{1}{4} \times \frac{1}{4} = \frac{37}{4} \times \frac{1}{4} = \frac{37}{16} = 2\frac{5}{16}''$

23) $\frac{8}{1} \times \frac{1}{5} = \frac{8}{5} = 1\frac{3}{5}''$

ANSWER KEY

PERCENT

Page 64, **Converting Percents to Decimals**

1) 0.18
2) 0.25
3) 0.32
4) 0.88

5) 0.06
6) 0.03
7) 0.09
8) 0.138

9) 0.216
10) 0.7451
11) 1.0
12) 2.0

13) 2.5 = 0.025
14) 26.25 = 0.2625

15) 36.25 = 0.3625
16) 18.7 = 0.187

17) 215.5 = 2.155
18) 9.25 = 0.0925

19) 122.75 = 1.2275
20) 2.8 = 0.028

Page 65, **Converting Decimals to Percents**

1) 25%
2) 50%
3) 75%
4) 100%

5) 11%
6) 17%
7) 39%
8) 86%

9) 4%
10) 12%
11) 7%
12) 11.5%

13) 25.6%
14) 33.3%
15) 174%
16) 18.5%

17) 74%
18) 12.34%
19) 121%
20) 99.8%

Page 66, **Converting Percents to Fractions**

1) $\frac{75}{100} = \frac{3}{4}$
2) $\frac{25}{100} = \frac{1}{4}$
3) $\frac{50}{100} = \frac{1}{2}$
4) $\frac{60}{100} = \frac{6}{10} = \frac{3}{5}$

5) $\frac{39}{100}$
6) $\frac{45}{100} = \frac{9}{20}$
7) $\frac{119}{100} = 1\frac{19}{100}$
8) $\frac{125}{100} = 1\frac{25}{100} = 1\frac{1}{4}$

9) $\frac{300}{100} = 3$
10) $\frac{800}{100} = 8$
11) $\frac{1100}{100} = 11$
12) $\frac{80}{100} = \frac{8}{10} = \frac{4}{5}$

13) $\frac{177}{1000}$
14) $\frac{213}{1000}$

15) $\frac{47}{1000}$
16) $\frac{105}{1000} = \frac{21}{200}$

Page 67, **Converting Fractions to Percents**

1) 0.25 = 25%   2) 0.50 = 50%   3) 0.75 = 75%   4) 0.10 = 10%

5) 0.125 = 12.5%   6) 0.625 = 62.5%

7) 0.70 = 70%   8) 0.1875 = 18.75%

9) 0.875 = 87.5%   10) 0.4375 = 43.75%

11) 5.80 = 580%   12) 0.0625 = 6.25%

13) 25.00 = 2 500%   14) 9.3125 = 931.25%

15) 0.09375 = 9.375%   16) 1.03125 = 103.125%

17) 0.6875 = 68.75%   18) 8.75 = 875%

19) 1.50 = 150%   20) 3.90 = 390%

Page 68, **Complete the table below with the missing percent, decimal or fraction.**

Percent	Decimal	Fraction
6.25%	0.0625	$\frac{1}{16}$
12.5%	0.125	$\frac{1}{8}$
18.75%	0.1875	$\frac{3}{16}$
25%	0.25	$\frac{1}{4}$
31.25%	0.3125	$\frac{5}{16}$
37.5%	0.375	$\frac{3}{8}$
43.75%	0.4375	$\frac{7}{16}$
50%	0.50	$\frac{1}{2}$
56.25%	0.5625	$\frac{9}{16}$
62.5%	0.625	$\frac{5}{8}$
68.75%	0.6875	$\frac{11}{16}$
75%	0.75	$\frac{3}{4}$
81.25%	0.8125	$\frac{13}{16}$
87.5%	0.875	$\frac{7}{8}$
93.75%	0.9375	$\frac{15}{16}$
100%	1.00	1

Page 70, **Calculating the Percentage of a Number**

1) $0.10 \times 100 = 10$ 2) $0.25 \times 200 = 50$ 3) $0.45 \times 75 = 33.75$

4) $0.07 \times 50 = 3.5$ 5) $0.45 \times 25 = 11.25$ 6) $0.11 \times 60 = 6.6$

7) $0.75 \times 350 = 262.5$ 8) $0.39 \times 80 = 31.2$

9) $1.15 \times 65 = 74.75$ 10) $1.25 \times 200 = 250$

11) $1.10 \times 100 = 110$ 12) $0.14 \times 35 = 4.9$

13) $0.105 \times 80 = 8.4$ 14) $0.30 \times 180 = 54$

15) $0.225 \times 360 = 81$ 16) $0.375 \times 600 = 225$

Page 72, **Calculating the Rate**

1) $\frac{25}{525} = 0.048 = 4.8\%$ 2) $\frac{7}{65} = 0.108 = 10.8\%$ 3) $\frac{65}{1700} = 0.038 = 3.8\%$

4) $\frac{11}{45} = 0.244 = 24.4\%$ 5) $\frac{4}{15} = 0.267 = 26.7\%$ 6) $\frac{75}{180} = 0.417 = 41.7\%$

7) $\frac{34}{100} = 0.34 = 34\%$ 8) $\frac{14}{199} = 0.07 = 7\%$ 9) $\frac{10}{100} = 0.1 = 10\%$

10) $\frac{10}{200} = 0.05 = 5\%$ 11) $\frac{9}{100} = 0.09 = 9\%$ 12) $\frac{41}{100} = 0.41 = 41\%$

13) $\frac{36}{3255} = 0.011 = 1.1\%$ 14) $\frac{8}{70} = 0.114 = 11.4\%$

15) $\frac{186}{750} = 0.248 = 24.8\%$ 16) $\frac{95}{220} = 0.432 = 43.2\%$

Page 74, **Calculating the Base**

1) $\frac{30}{0.25} = 120$ 2) $\frac{86}{0.10} = 860$ 3) $\frac{5}{0.75} = 6.7$

4) $\frac{65}{0.14} = 464.3$ 5) $\frac{45}{0.80} = 56.3$ 6) $\frac{15}{0.12} = 125$

7) $\frac{21}{0.42} = 50$ 8) $\frac{100}{0.15} = 666.7$ 9) $\frac{4}{0.25} = 16$

10) $\frac{75}{0.12} = 625$ 11) $\frac{100}{0.20} = 500$ 12) $\frac{61.5}{0.10} = 615$

13) $\frac{14.7}{0.05} = 294$ 14) $\frac{125}{0.75} = 166.7$ 15) $\frac{21}{0.30} = 70$

16) $\frac{15.5}{0.07} = 221.4$

Page 76, **Calculating an Increase**

1) P = 45 × 1.10 = 49.5
The total amount of concrete required is 49.5 cubic yards.

2) $\dfrac{439}{392}$ = R

1.119 = R
111.9%
111.989 – 100 = 11.989%
The percentage of waste is 12%.

3) $\dfrac{13\ 500}{1.125}$ = B

12 000 = B
The contractor's original costs were $12 000.

Page 78, **Calculating a Decrease**

1) P = 0.75 × 1 200 = 900 pounds

2) P = 0.90 × 2 000 = 1 800 pounds

3) P = 0.80 × $215 = $172.00

Page 78, **Practice**

1) Total tax = 7% PST + 7% GST = 14%
a) P = 0.14 × $3 776 = $528.64
b) Total paid = $3 776 + $528.64 = $4 304.64

2) a) P = 0.6 × 35 = 21 columns
b) P = 0.4 × 35 = 14 columns
You could also subtract 21 from 35 to get the number of columns poured in the afternoon.

3) P = .875 × 3 208 = 2 807

4) P = 0.21 × $34 850 = $7 318.50

5) P = 0.16 × $2 845.50 = $455.28

6) $\frac{20}{32}$ = R
0.625 = R
0.625 = 62.5%

7) $\dfrac{256.20}{1\ 220.00}$ = R

0.21 = R
0.21 = 21%

8) $\dfrac{6\ 534}{43\ 560} = R$

 $0.15 = R$
 $0.15 = 15\%$

9) a) $P = 0.85 \times \$254.80 = \$216.58$

 b) $P = 0.85 \times \$12.60 = \$10.71$

 c) $P = 0.85 \times \$38.40 = \$32.64$

10) a) $\dfrac{2\ 412}{3\ 216} = R$

 $0.75 = R$
 $0.75 = 75\%$

 b) $100\% - 75\% = 25\%$

11) $P = 125\% \times 125 = 1.25 \times 125 = 156.25$ square metres

12) a) $P = 0.65 \times \$4\ 375 = \$2\ 843.75$

 b) $\$4\ 375.00 - \$2\ 843.75 = \$1\ 531.25$

13) a) $P = 0.78 \times \$8\ 520 = \$6\ 645.60$

 b) $\$8\ 520.00 - \$6\ 645.60 = \$1\ 874.40$

14) $P = 0.45 \times 8\ 545 = 3\ 845.25$ hours

15) $P = 1.045 \times \$585.00 = \$611.33$

16) a) 75%

 b) $P = 0.75 \times \$25.40 = \$19.05$

 c) $P = 0.7 \times \$25.40 = \$17.78$

 d) $P = 0.9 \times \$25.40 = \$22.86$

ANSWER KEY

RATIO AND PROPORTION

Page 86, Simplifying Ratios

1) $\dfrac{2}{1}$ 2) $\dfrac{1}{4}$ 3) $\dfrac{1}{3}$ 4) $\dfrac{9}{1}$

5) $\dfrac{4}{1}$ 6) $\dfrac{5}{1}$ 7) $\dfrac{4}{1}$ 8) $\dfrac{2}{1}$

9) $\dfrac{3}{1}$ 10) $\dfrac{6}{1}$ 11) $\dfrac{1}{15}$ 12) $\dfrac{6}{1}$

Page 89, Solving a Direct Proportion

1) $\chi = 4$ 2) $\chi = 12$ 3) $\chi = 8$

4) $\chi = 20$ 5) $\chi = 6$ 6) $\chi = 90$

7) $\chi = 32$ 8) $\chi = 225$ 9) $\chi = 9$

10) $\chi = 16$ 11) $\chi = 60.72$ 12) $\chi = 1\,250$

13) $\chi = 28$ 14) $\chi = 10.8$ 15) $\chi = 28$

16) $\chi = 6$

Page 90, Solving Similar Triangles

1) A = 2 500 mm   2) B = 3 mm

3) C = 6 000 mm   4) D = 189.6 mm

5) E = 652 mm   6) F = 625 mm

7) G = 400 mm   8) $15 \div 6 = 2.5$ mm
   H = 600 mm   I = 2 mm
                    J = 4 mm
                    K = 6 mm
                    L = 8 mm
                    M = 10 mm

9) N = 2.3 mm   10) P = 546.88 mm

11) Q = 1 485 mm   12) R = 750 mm

Page 97, **Solving an Indirect Proportion**

1) $\dfrac{5}{9} = \dfrac{\chi \text{ days}}{80}$

$\dfrac{400}{9} = \chi$

$44.4 = \chi$

2) $\dfrac{8}{11} = \dfrac{\chi \text{ days}}{26}$

$\dfrac{208}{11} = \chi$

$18.9 = \chi$

3) $\dfrac{220 \text{ lbs applied force}}{\chi} = \dfrac{6 \text{ in lever arm}}{58 \text{ in lever arm}}$

$\dfrac{12\ 760}{6} = \chi$

$2\ 126.7 = \chi$

4) $\dfrac{180 \text{ lbs applied force}}{\chi} = \dfrac{4.5 \text{ in}}{55.5 \text{ in}}$

$\dfrac{9\ 990}{4.5} = \chi$

$2\ 200 = \chi$

Page 99, **Using Rates to Compare**

1)   Journeyperson   Apprentice

$\dfrac{2}{3} = 0.667$ $\dfrac{2}{6.75} = 0.296$

$0.667 + 0.296 = 0.963$ hours

$\dfrac{\chi}{2 \text{ doors}} = \dfrac{60 \text{ minutes}}{0.963 \text{ hours}}$

$\chi \times 0.963 = 60 \times 2$

$\chi = \dfrac{120}{0.963}$

$\chi = 124.6106$ minutes

$124.6106 \div 60 = 2.0768$ hours

$0.0768 \times 60 = 4.6$ minutes

It will take the journeyperson and the apprentice 2 hours and 5 minutes to install 2 doors.

Page 100, **Practice**

1) $\dfrac{7}{2} = \dfrac{12 \text{ m}^3}{\chi}$

$\chi = \dfrac{24}{7} = 3.4 \text{ m}^3$

2)a. $\dfrac{1}{0.75} = \dfrac{\chi}{6}$

$\dfrac{6}{0.75} = \chi$

$8' = \chi$

b. $\dfrac{1}{0.75} = \dfrac{\chi}{8.5 \text{ feet}}$

$\dfrac{8.5}{0.75} = \chi$

$11.3 \text{ feet} = \chi$

c. $\dfrac{1}{0.75} = \dfrac{2\ 500\ \text{mm}}{\chi}$

$2\ 500 \times 0.75 = \chi$

$1\ 875\ \text{mm} = \chi$

d. $\dfrac{1}{0.75} = \dfrac{3\ 200\ \text{mm}}{\chi}$

$3\ 200 \times 0.75 = \chi$

$2\ 400\ \text{mm} = \chi$

3) $\dfrac{3.6\ \text{kg}}{90\ \text{m}^2} = \dfrac{\chi}{2\ 500\ \text{m}^2}$

$3.6 \times 2\ 500\ \text{m}^2 = \chi \times 90\ \text{m}^2$

$\dfrac{9\ 000}{90} = \chi$

$100\ \text{kg} = \chi$

4)

	A	**B**	**C**	**D**
a.	15 mm	20 mm	54 mm	72 mm
b.	180 mm	240 mm	480 mm	640 mm
c.	35 m	45 m	105 mm	135 m
d.	22 m	38 m	48 m	82.9 m

5) cement

$\dfrac{1}{10} = \dfrac{\chi}{86\ \text{m}^3}$

$\dfrac{86}{10} = \chi$

8.6 m³ cement

sand

$\dfrac{3}{10} = \dfrac{\chi}{86\ \text{m}^3}$

$\dfrac{258}{10} = \chi$

25.8 m³ sand

gravel

$\dfrac{6}{10} = \dfrac{\chi}{86\ \text{m}^3}$

$\dfrac{516}{10} = \chi$

51.6 m³ gravel

6) $\dfrac{6 \text{ carpenters}}{4 \text{ carpenters}} = \dfrac{\chi \text{ hours}}{5 \text{ hours}}$

$6 \times 5 = \chi \times 4$

$\dfrac{30}{4} = \chi$

$7.5 \text{ hours} = \chi$

7) $\dfrac{8 \text{ carpenters}}{\chi \text{ carpenters}} = \dfrac{4 \text{ days}}{5 \text{ days}}$

$8 \times 5 = 4 \times \chi$

$\dfrac{40}{4} = \chi$

$10 \text{ carpenters} = \chi$

8) $\dfrac{3}{5} = \dfrac{\chi}{8.75}$ $\dfrac{4}{5} = \dfrac{\chi}{8.75}$

$3 \times 8.75 = \chi \times 5$ $4 \times 8.75 = \chi \times 5$

$\dfrac{26.25}{5} = \chi$ $\dfrac{35}{5} = \chi$

$5.25 \text{ cm} = \chi$ $7 \text{ cm} = \chi$

ANSWER KEY

MEASUREMENT AND CONVERSION

Page 106, **Converting Within the Imperial System**

1)	12 in	2)	24 in
3)	42 in	4)	93 in
5)	71 in	6)	4 ft 8 in
7)	10 ft 6 in	8)	18 ft 5 in
9)	3 ft = 36 in	10)	9 ft = 108 in
11)	18 ft = 216 in	12)	144 in^2
13)	432 in^2	14)	9 ft^2 = 1 296 in^2
15)	36 ft^2 = 5 184 in^2	16)	9 ft^2
17)	7 ft^2	18)	1 ft^3
19)	5 ft^3	20)	7.5 ft^3
21)	6 912 in^3	22)	27 ft^3
23)	10 yd^3	24)	37.44 Imperial gallons
25)	53.04 Imperial gallons	26)	3.85 ft^3
27)	7.37 ft^3	28)	82.5 US gal
29)	22.5 US gallons	30)	4 ft^3

Page 107, **Measuring Fractions**

1) two

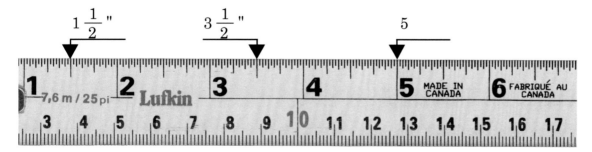

2) four

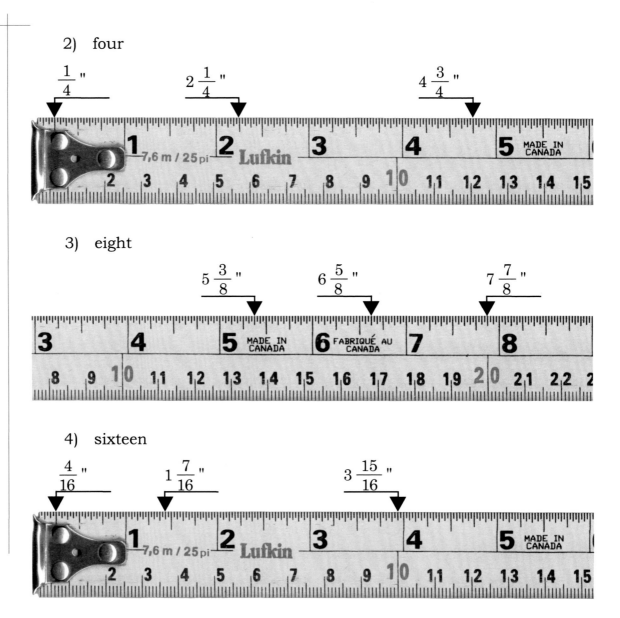

3) eight

4) sixteen

Page 108, **Measuring Fractions**

1)

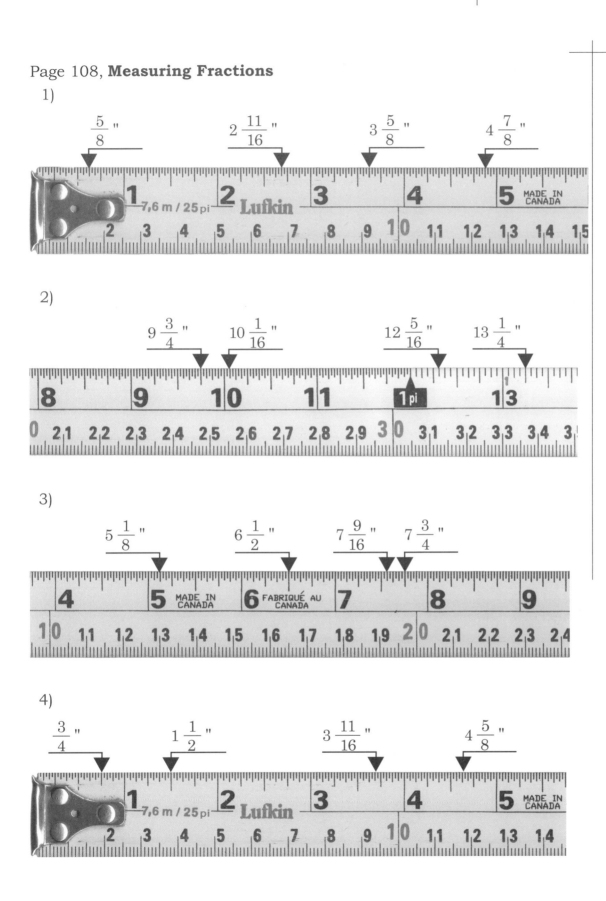

2)

3)

4)

Page 109, **Measuring Fractions**

1) $4\frac{1}{2}$ inches
2) $1\frac{3}{8}$ inches
3) $2\frac{1}{4}$ inches
4) $3\frac{5}{8}$ inches
5) $6\frac{1}{16}$ inches
6) $1\frac{15}{16}$ inches
7) $3\frac{3}{4}$ inches
8) $3\frac{7}{16}$ inches
9) $6\frac{1}{4}$ inches
10) $5\frac{3}{4}$ inches

Page 111, **Adding and Subtracting Feet and Inches**

1) 11 ft
2) 1 ft 10 in
3) 2 ft 1 in
4) 17 ft 7 in
5) 5 ft 3 in
6) 4 ft 7 in
7) 11 in
8) 33 ft 3 in
9) 6 ft 5 in
10) 8 ft 8 in
11) $12 \text{ ft } 8\frac{7}{8}$ in
12) $37 \text{ ft } 11\frac{13}{16}$ in
13) $9 \text{ ft } 2\frac{5}{8}$ in
14) $20 \text{ ft } 8\frac{1}{4}$ in
15) $46 \text{ ft } 2\frac{9}{16}$ in

Page 116, **Converting Units**

1) 10 mm
2) 1 000 mm
3) 100 cm
4) 8 000 mm
5) 3.5 cm
6) 15.5 cm
7) 1 cm^2
8) 9 cm^2
9) 3.75 cm^2
10) 600 mm^2
11) $1\ 700 \text{ mm}^2$
12) 1 m^2
13) 5 m^2
14) 9.5 m^2
15) 1 L
16) 11 L

17) 4.5 L

18) 10 000 mL

19) 22 000 mL

20) 1 400 mL

21) 3 200 mL

22) 1 000 000 mg

23) 6 000 000 mg

24) 2 700 000 mg

25) 1 000 000 cm³

26) 4 000 000 cm³

27) 6 400 000 cm³

28) 1 m³

29) 8 m³

30) 2.5 m³

Page 118, **Measuring Centimetres and Millimetres**

1)

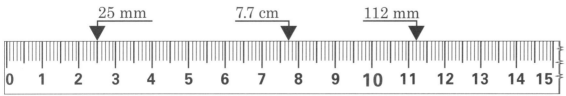

2)

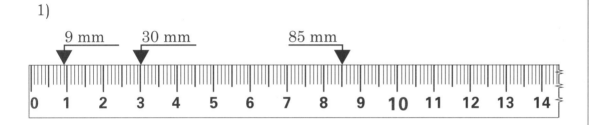

3)

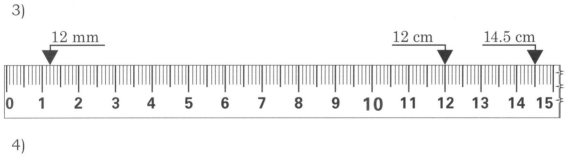

4)

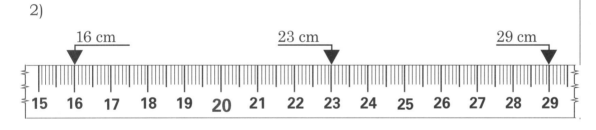

Page 119, **Measuring Centimetres and Millimetres**

1)

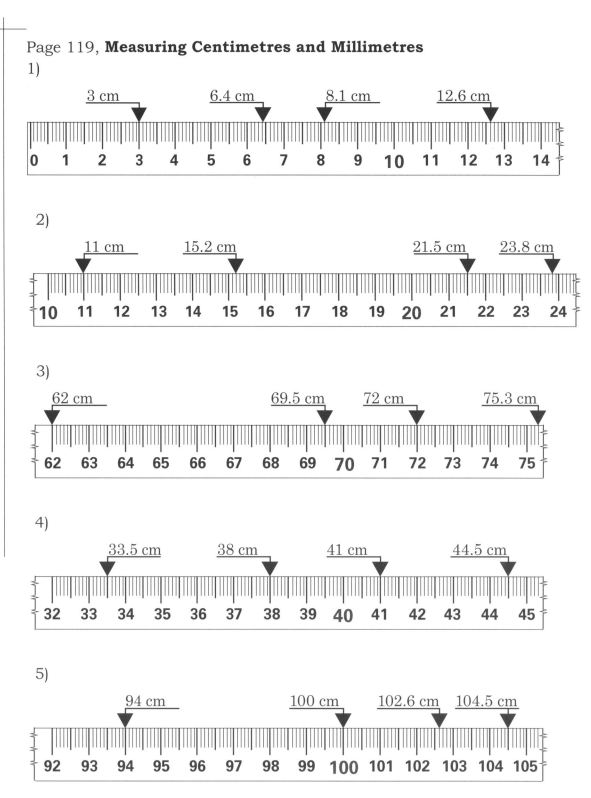

2)

3)

4)

5)

Page 120, **Measuring Centimetres and Millimetres**

1) 60 mm, 6 cm, .06 m

2) 74 mm, 7.4 cm, .074 m

3) 35 mm, 3.5 cm, .035 m

4) 58 mm, 5.8 cm, .058 m

5) 40 mm, 4 cm, .04 m

6) 55 mm, 5.5 cm, .055 m

7) 66 mm, 6.6 cm, .066 m

8) 45 mm, 4.5 cm, .045 m

9) 82 mm, 8.2 cm, .082 m

10) 50 mm, 5 cm, .05 m

Page 122, **Converting Between Metric and Imperial**

1)	a) 2.54 cm	b) 17.78 cm	c) 381 mm
2)	a) 1.97"	b) 29.53"	c) 41.34"
3)	a) 1 m	b) 2.15 m	c) 0.92 m
4)	a) 234"	b) 97.5"	c) 26 ft
5)	a) 1 m^3	b) 3.85 m^3	c) 6.08 m^3
6)	a) 3.9 yd^3	b) 11.96 yd^3	c) 6.5 yd^3
7)	a) 2.2 lb	b) 26.4 lb	c) 34.32 lb
8)	a) 11.36 kg	b) 29.09 kg	c) 58.18 kg

ANSWER KEY

GEOMETRY - PERIMETER

Page 140, **Calculating Perimeter**

    1)   P = 2(L + W) = 2(47.8 + 39.3 cm) = 174.2 cm

    2)   2 ft = 24 in

        P = 2(L + W) = 2(18 + 28) = 92 in

    3)   C = πd = π × 29 = 91.11 mm

    4)   diameter = 2 × r = 2 × 15 = 30 cm

        C = πd = π × 30 = 94.25 cm

    5)   C = πd = π × 9 = 28.27 in

    6)   diameter = 2 × r = 2 × 2.4 = 4.8 ft

        C = πd = π × 4.8 = 15.08 ft

    7)   125 cm = 1.25 m

        $P = s^1 + s^2 + s^3 + s^4 = 2 + 1.25 + 1.2 + 1.25 = 5.7$ m

    8)   18 in = 1.5 ft

        $P = s^1 + s^2 + s^3 + s^4 = 5 + 2 + 1.5 + 2 = 10.5$ ft

    9) $P = s^1 + s^2 + s^3 = 25 + 45 + 25 = 95$ cm

  10)   12 in = 1 ft

        $P = s^1 + s^2 + s^3 = 3 + 1 + 3.5 = 7.5$ ft

  11)   55 cm = 0.55 m

        $P = s^1 + s^2 + s^3 + s^4 = 1.2 + 0.55 + 1.2 + 0.55 = 3.5$ m

  12) $P = s^1 + s^2 + s^3 + s^4 = 15 + 29 + 15 + 29 = 88$ in

  13)   P = 6s = 6 × 15 = 90 mm

  14)   P = 6s = 6 × 3.1 = 18.6 ft

Page 143, **Calculating a Side when you know the Perimeter**

    1)   c = πd   2)   c = πd

        3.2 = πd   15.8 = πd

        $\dfrac{3.2}{\pi} = d$ $\dfrac{15.8}{\pi} = d$

        1.02 ft = d   5.03 m = d

3) $c = \pi d$

    $39 = \pi d$

    $\dfrac{39}{\pi} = d$

    $12.41 = d$

    radius = $12.41 \div 2 = 6.21$ in

4) $P = 2(L + W)$

    $112 = 2(L + 12.5)$

    $112 = 2L + 25$

    $112 - 25 = 2L$

    $\dfrac{87}{2} = L$

    43.50 ft = L

5) $P = 2(L + W)$

    $865 = 2(310 + W)$

    $865 = 620 + 2W$

    $865 - 620 = 2W$

    $\dfrac{245}{2} = W$

    122.50 mm = W

6) 4 ft – 6 in = 4.5 ft

    1 ft – 9 in = 1.75 ft

    $P = 2(L + W)$

    $4.5 = 2(1.75 + W)$

    $4.5 = 3.5 + 2W$

    $4.5 - 3.5 = 2W$

    $\dfrac{1.0}{2} = W$

    0.50 ft = W

Page 146, **Calculating the Perimeter of Complex Shapes**

1) $C = \pi d = \pi \times 150 = 471.24$ mm
Total perimeter = $471.24 + 250 + 250 = 971.24$ mm

2) 3' - 4" = 3.33'
6' - 8" = 6.67'
$C = \pi d = \pi \times 3.33 = 10.46'$
Total perimeter = $10.46 + 6.67 + 6.67 = 23.8'$

3) $C = \pi d = \pi \times 4 = 12.57'$
Length of one side = $88 - 2 \times r = 88 - 2 \times 2 = 88 - 4 = 84'$
Total perimeter = $12.57 + 84 + 84 = 180.57'$

4) $C = \pi d = \pi \times 28 = 87.96$ in
Circumference of half a circle = $87.96 \div 2 = 43.98$ in
Total perimeter = $43.98 + 20 + 28 + 20 = 111.98$ in

5) 29 in = 2.42 ft
$C = \pi d = \pi \times 2.42 = 7.6$ ft
Circumference of half a circle = $7.6 \div 2 = 3.8$ ft
Total perimeter = $3.8 + 2 + 2.42 + 2 = 10.22$ ft

6)   Missing side$_1$ = 17 − 4 = 13"
        Missing side$_2$ = 20 − 5 = 15"
        Total perimeter = 17 + 20 + 4 + 15 + 13 + 5 = 74"

7)   550 cm = 5.50 m
        P = 5.5 + 6 + 5.5 + 2 + 3.5 = 22.5 m

8)   diameter = radius × 2 = 0.8 × 2 = 1.6 m
        C = πd = π × 1.6 = 5.03 m
        Circumference of three-quarters of a circle = 5.03 × 0.75 = 3.77 m
        Total circumference = 3.77 + 0.8 + 0.8 = 5.37 m

9) $9\frac{1}{4}$" = 9.25"
        C = πd = π × 9.25 = 29.06"
        Circumference of a half-circle = 29.06 ÷ 2 = 14.53"
        Total circumference = 14.53 + 9.25 = 23.78"

10)   C = πd = π × 2.4 = 7.54 ft
        Circumference of a half-circle = 7.54 ÷ 2 = 3.77 ft
        Total perimeter = 3.77 + 2.4 + 2.4 = 8.57 ft

Answer Key

Geometry - Area

Page 152, Calculating Area

1) $A = L \times W = 6 \text{ m} \times 3 \text{ m} = 18 \text{ m}^2$

2) $A = L \times W = 5 \text{ ft} \times 3 \text{ ft} = 15 \text{ ft}^2$

3) $A = s^2 = (9 \text{ cm})^2 = 81 \text{ cm}^2$

4) $A = s^2 = (15 \text{ in})^2 = 225 \text{ in}^2$

5) $A = \dfrac{bh}{2} = \dfrac{80 \text{ mm} \times 125 \text{ mm}}{2} = \dfrac{10\,000}{2} = 5\,000 \text{ mm}^2$

6) $A = \dfrac{bh}{2} = \dfrac{7 \text{ ft} \times 3 \text{ ft}}{2} = \dfrac{21}{2} = 10.5 \text{ ft}^2$

7) $A = \pi r^2 = \pi \times (4 \text{ m})^2 = 50.27 \text{ m}^2$

8) $A = \pi r^2 = \pi \times (9 \text{ in})^2 = 254.47 \text{ in}^2$

9) $r = \dfrac{d}{2} = \dfrac{7}{2} = 3.5 \text{ cm}$

   $A = \pi r^2 = \pi \times (3.5 \text{ cm})^2 = 38.48 \text{ cm}^2$

10) $r = \dfrac{d}{2} = \dfrac{2 \text{ ft}}{2} = 1 \text{ ft}$

    $A = \pi r^2 = \pi \times (1 \text{ ft}^2) = 3.14 \text{ ft}^2$

11) $A = bh = 4 \text{ m} \times 5 \text{ m} = 20 \text{ m}^2$

12) $A = bh = 4 \text{ ft} \times 6 \text{ ft} = 24 \text{ ft}^2$

13) $A = \left(\dfrac{b_1 + b_2}{2}\right) h = \left(\dfrac{150 \text{ mm} + 80 \text{ mm}}{2}\right) 75 \text{ mm} = \left(\dfrac{230}{2}\right) 75 =$
    $115 \times 75 = 8\,625 \text{ mm}^2$

14) $A = \left(\dfrac{b_1 + b_2}{2}\right) h = \left(\dfrac{9 \text{ ft} + 4.5 \text{ ft}}{2}\right) 3 = \left(\dfrac{13.5}{2}\right) 3 \text{ ft} = 6.75 \times 3 = 20.25 \text{ ft}^2$

15) $A = 2.59 \times s^2 = 2.59 \times (45 \text{ mm})^2 = 5\,244.75 \text{ mm}^2$

16) $A = 2.59 \times s^2 = 2.59 \times (7 \text{ in})^2 = 126.91 \text{ in}^2$

17) $75 \text{ cm} = 0.75 \text{ m}$
    $A = L \times W = 2 \text{ m} \times 0.75 \text{ m} = 1.5 \text{ m}^2$

18) 36 in = 3 ft

$$A = \frac{bh}{2} = \frac{3 \text{ ft} \times 3 \text{ ft}}{2} = \frac{9}{2} = 4.5 \text{ ft}^2$$

19) 125 mm = 0.125 m

A = bh = 0.125 m × 1.2 m = 0.15 m²

20) 46 in = 3.83 ft, 23 in = 1.92 ft

$$A = \left(\frac{b_1 + b_2}{2}\right)h = \left(\frac{3.83 \text{ ft} + 1.92 \text{ ft}}{2}\right)2 \text{ ft} = \left(\frac{5.75}{2}\right)2 =$$
2.875 × 2 = 5.75 ft²

21) Radius $= \frac{d}{2} = \frac{6 \text{ in}}{2} = 3$ in

A = πr² = π × (3 in)² = 28.27 in²

22) 125 cm = 1.25 m

$$A = \frac{bh}{2} = \frac{2.5 \text{ m} \times 1.25 \text{ m}}{2} = \frac{3.125}{2} = 1.56 \text{ m}^2$$

23) 4 ft – 6 in = 4.5 ft

2 ft – 4 in = 2.33 ft

A = LW = 4.5 ft × 2.33 ft = 10.49 ft²

24) A = s² = (6.38 cm)² = 40.7 cm²

25) A = 2.59 × s² = 2.59 × (1.1 m)² = 3.13 m²

26) 150 cm = 1.5 m

$$A = \frac{bh}{2} = \frac{1.5 \text{ m} \times 0.8 \text{ m}}{2} = \frac{1.2}{2} = 0.6 \text{ m}^2$$

Page 159, Calculating the Area of Complex Shapes

1) A = L × W = 4.5 m × 5 m = 22.5 m²
A = L × W = 2.5 m × 3 m = 7.5 m²
Total Area = 22.5 m² + 7.5 m² = 30 m²

2) A = L × W = 5.2 m × 3 m = 15.6 m²
A = L × W = 1.2 m × 1.5 m = 1.8 m²
Total Area = 15.6 m² + 1.8 m² = 17.4 m²

3) Area of rectangle = 6 m × 1.2 m = 7.2 m²
radius $= \frac{d}{2} = \frac{1.2 \text{ m}}{2} = 0.6$ m
Area of circle = πr² = π × (0.6 m)² = 1.13 m²
Total Area = 1.13 m² + 7.2 m² = 8.33 m²

4) 240 m – (45 + 45) = 150 m
Area of rectangle = 150 m × 90 m = 13 500 m^2
Radius = diameter ÷ 2 = 90 m ÷ 2 = 45 m
Area of circle = πr^2 = π × (45 m)^2 = 6 361.73 m^2
Total area = 13 500 m^2 + 6 361.73 m^2 = 19 861.73 m^2

5) Area of rectangle = LW = 5 ft × 3 ft = 15 ft^2
Radius = diameter ÷ 2 = 5 ÷ 2 = 2.5 ft
Area of circle = πr^2 = π × (2.5 ft)^2 = 19.63 ft^2
Area of half circle = 19.63 ft^2 ÷ 2 = 9.82 ft^2
Total area = 15 ft^2 + 9.82 ft^2 = 24.82 ft^2

6) Area of rectangle = LW = 10 m × 17 m = 170 m^2
Radius = diameter ÷ 2 = 10 ÷ 2 = 5 m
Area of circle = πr^2 = π × (5 m)^2 = 78.54 m^2
Area of half circle = 78.54 m^2 ÷ 2 = 39.27 m^2
Total area = 170 m^2 + 39.27 m^2 = 209.27 m^2

7) Length of big rectangle = 7 ft + 20 ft + 9 ft = 36 ft
Width of big rectangle = 8 ft + 18 ft + 8 ft = 34 ft
Area of big rectangle = LW = 36 ft × 34 ft = 1 224 ft^2
Area of small rectangle = LW = 10 ft × 18 ft = 180 ft^2
Area of trapezoid =

$$\left(\frac{b_1 + b_2}{2}\right)h = \left(\frac{20 \text{ ft} + 10 \text{ ft}}{2}\right)8 \text{ ft} = \left(\frac{30}{2}\right)8 = 15 \times 8 = 120 \text{ ft}^2$$

Total area = 1 224 ft^2 – (180 ft^2 + 120 ft^2) = 1 224 ft^2 – 300 ft^2 = 924 ft^2

8) Area of big rectangle = LW = 3.5 m × 3.9 m = 13.65 m^2
Area of square = s^2 = (0.9 m)^2 = 0.81 m^2
Area of small rectangle = LW = 0.9 m × 1.3 m = 1.17 m^2
Total area = 13.65 m^2 – (0.81 m^2 + 1.17 m^2) =
13.65 m^2 – 1.98 m^2 = 11.67 m^2

9) Area of square = s^2 = (4 cm)^2 = 16 cm^2
Area of triangle = $\dfrac{bh}{2}$ = $\dfrac{4 \text{ cm} \times 5 \text{ cm}}{2}$ = $\dfrac{20 \text{ cm}}{2}$ = 10 cm^2

Total area = 16 cm^2 + 10 cm^2 = 26 cm^2

10) Area of triangle = $\dfrac{bh}{2}$ = $\dfrac{12.8 \text{ cm} \times 11.1 \text{ cm}}{2}$ = $\dfrac{142.08 \text{ cm}}{2}$ = 71.04 cm^2

Radius = diameter ÷ 2 = 12.8 ÷ 2 = 6.4 cm
Area of circle = πr^2 = π × (6.4 cm)^2 = 128.68 cm^2
Area of half circle = 128.68 cm^2 ÷ 2 = 64.34 cm^2
Total area = 71.04 cm^2 + 64.34 cm^2 = 135.38 cm^2

11)   Radius = diameter ÷ 2 = 20 in ÷ 2 = 10 in

Area of big circle = $\pi r^2 = \pi \times (10\ \text{in})^2 = 314.16\ \text{in}^2$

Radius = diameter ÷ 2 = 6 in ÷ 2 = 3 in

Area of small circle = $\pi r^2 = \pi \times (3\ \text{in})^2 = 28.27\ \text{in}^2$

Total area = 314.16 in² – 28.27 in² = 285.89 in²

12)   Convert mm to m.

2 140 mm = 2.14 m

8 440 mm = 8.44 m

Area of triangle =

$$\frac{bh}{2} = \frac{8.44\ \text{m} \times 2.38\ \text{m}}{2} = \frac{20.09}{2} = 10.05\ \text{m}^2$$

Area of trapezoid =

$$\left(\frac{b_1 + b_2}{2}\right)h = \left(\frac{12.72\ \text{m} + 8.44\ \text{m}}{2}\right)3.88\ \text{m} = \left(\frac{21.16}{2}\right)3.88 =$$

10.58 × 3.88 = 41.05 m²

Total area = 41.05 m² + 10.05 m² = 51.10 m²

13)   Area of rectangle = LW = 30 ft × 14 ft = 420 ft²

Area of triangle = $\dfrac{bh}{2} = \dfrac{9\ \text{ft} \times 7\ \text{ft}}{2} = \dfrac{63}{2} = 31.5\ \text{ft}^2$

The two triangles are the same.

Two triangles = 31.5 ft² × 2 = 63 ft²

Total area = 420 ft² – 63 ft² = 357 ft²

14)   Area of trapezoid =

$$\left(\frac{b_1 + b_2}{2}\right)h = \left(\frac{120\ \text{ft} + 80\ \text{ft}}{2}\right)75\ \text{ft} = \left(\frac{200}{2}\right)75 = 100 \times 75 = 7\ 500\ \text{ft}^2$$

Area of house = LW = 50 ft × 25 ft = 1 250 ft²

Area of driveway = LW = 9 ft × 20 ft = 180 ft²

Total area = 7 500 ft² – (1 250 ft² + 180 ft²) =

7 500 ft² – 1 430 ft² = 6 070 ft²

15)   Area of rectangle = LW = 21 mm × 9 mm = 189 mm²

Area of trapezoid =

$$\left(\frac{b_1 + b_2}{2}\right)h = \left(\frac{7\ \text{mm} + 4\ \text{mm}}{2}\right)14\ \text{mm} = \left(\frac{11}{2}\right)14 = 5.5 \times 14 = 77\ \text{mm}^2$$

Total area = 189 mm² + 77 mm² = 266 mm²

16) Area of rectangle = LW = 8.5 cm × 3 cm = 25.5 cm²
Area of trapezoid =

$$\left(\frac{b_1 + b_2}{2}\right)h = \left(\frac{14.5\ cm + 8.5\ cm}{2}\right)9\ cm = \left(\frac{23}{2}\right)9 =$$

11.5 × 9 = 103.5 mm²
There are two trapezoids that are the same.
Two trapezoids = 103.5 cm² × 2 = 207 cm²
Total area = 25.5 cm² + 207 cm² = 232.5 cm²

17) Radius = diameter ÷ 2 = 14.5 ft ÷ 2 = 7.25 ft
Area of circle = πr² = π × (7.25 ft)² = 165.13 ft²
Area of square = s² = (2.1 ft)² = 4.41 ft²
Total area = 165.13 ft² − 4.41 ft² = 160.72 ft²

18) Length of b_1 = 51 ft + 32 ft + 32 ft + 51 ft = 166 ft
Area of trapezoid =

$$\left(\frac{b_1 + b_2}{2}\right)h = \left(\frac{166\ ft + 46\ ft}{2}\right)91\ ft = \left(\frac{212}{2}\right)91 =$$

106 × 91 = 9 646 ft²
Area of circle = πr² = π × (32 ft)² = 3 216.99 ft²
Area of half circle = 3 216.99 ft² ÷ 2 = 1 608.50 ft²
Total area = 9 646 ft² − 1 608.50 ft² = 8 037.50 ft²

19) Convert inches to decimals of a foot.
9 ft — 6 in = 9.5 ft
Area of triangle = A = $\dfrac{bh}{2}$ = $\dfrac{9.5\ ft \times 3\ ft}{2}$ = $\dfrac{28.5}{2}$ = 14.25 ft²
Area of trapezoid =

$$\left(\frac{b_1 + b_2}{2}\right)h = \left(\frac{10 + 9.5}{2}\right)8\ ft = \left(\frac{19.5}{2}\right)8 = 9.75 \times 8 = 78\ ft^2$$

Total area = 14.25 ft² + 78 ft² = 92.25 ft²

20) Radius of big circle = diameter ÷ 2 = 500 mm ÷ 2 = 250 mm
Area of big circle = πr² = π × (250 mm)² = 196 349.54 mm²
Radius of inner circle = diameter ÷ 2 = 250 mm ÷ 2 = 125 mm
Area of inner circle = πr² = π × (125 mm)² = 49 087.39 mm²
Radius of small circle = diameter ÷ 2 = 30 mm ÷ 2 = 15 mm
Area of small circle = πr² = π × (15 mm)² = 706.86 mm²
Eight small circles = 8 × 706.86 mm² = 5 654.88 mm²
Total area = 196 349.54 mm² − (49 087.39 mm² + 5 654.88 mm²) =
196 349.54 mm² − 54 742.27 mm² = 141 607.27 mm²

Page 167, **Calculating One of the Sides when You Know the Area**

1) $A = L \times W$

   $25.6 \text{ m}^2 = L \times 2.5 \text{ m}$

   $\dfrac{25.6 \text{ m}^2}{2.5 \text{ m}} = L$

   $10.24 \text{ m} = L$

2) $A = L \times W$

   $89 \text{ in}^2 = 29 \text{ in} \times W$

   $\dfrac{89 \text{ in}^2}{29 \text{ in}} = W$

   $3.07 \text{ in} = W$

3) $A = \pi r^2$

   $\dfrac{37}{\pi} = r^2$

   $11.78 = r^2$

   $\sqrt{11.78} = r$

   $3.43 \text{ ft} = r$

4) $A = \pi r^2$

   $25 \text{ m}^2 = \pi \times r^2$

   $\dfrac{25}{\pi} = r^2$

   $7.96 = r^2$

   $\sqrt{7.96} = r$

   $2.82 \text{ m} = r$

   $d = 2.82 \times 2 = 5.64 \text{ m}$

5) $A = \dfrac{bh}{2}$

   $39.5 \text{ in}^2 = \dfrac{b \times 6 \text{ in}}{2}$

   $39.5 \text{ in}^2 \times 2 = b \times 6 \text{ in}$

   $79 = b \times 6 \text{ in}$

   $\dfrac{79 \text{ in}^2}{6 \text{ in}} = b$

   $13.17 \text{ in} = b$

6) $A = \dfrac{bh}{2}$

$220 \text{ cm}^2 = \dfrac{18.5 \text{ cm} \times h}{2}$

$220 \text{ cm}^2 \times 2 = 18.5 \text{ cm} \times h$

$440 \text{ cm}^2 = 18.5 \text{ cm} \times h$

$\dfrac{440 \text{ cm}^2}{18.5 \text{ cm}} = h$

$23.78 \text{ cm} = h$

7) $A = s^2$

$355 \text{ cm}^2 = s^2$

$\sqrt{355} = s$

$18.84 \text{ cm} = s$

8) $A = s^2$

$415 \text{ ft}^2 = s^2$

$\sqrt{415} \text{ ft} = s$

$20.37 \text{ ft} = s$

Page 173, **Lateral Area and Surface Area**

1) L.A. $= \pi d \times h = \pi \times 1.3 \text{ ft} \times 15 \text{ ft} = 61.26 \text{ ft}^2$
S.A. $=$ L.A. $+$ area of two bases $= 61.26 \text{ ft}^2 + (\pi r^2 \times 2) =$
$61.26 \text{ ft}^2 + (\pi \times 0.65 \text{ ft} \times 2) = 61.26 \text{ ft}^2 + 2.65 \text{ ft}^2 = 63.91 \text{ ft}^2$

2) L.A. $= \pi d \times h = \pi \times 0.15 \text{ m} \times 2.67 \text{ m} = 1.26 \text{ m}^2$
S.A. $=$ L.A. $+$ area of two bases $= 1.26 \text{ m}^2 + (\pi r^2 \times 2) =$
$1.26 \text{ m}^2 + (\pi \times (0.075 \text{ m})^2 \times 2) = 1.26 \text{ m}^2 + 0.04 \text{ m}^2 = 1.30 \text{ m}^2$

3) Area of front and back $= 2.5 \text{ ft} \times 4.67 \text{ ft} \times 2 = 23.35 \text{ ft}^2$
Area of sides $= 1 \text{ ft} \times 4.67 \text{ ft} \times 2 = 9.34 \text{ ft}^2$
L.A. $= 23.35 \text{ ft}^2 + 9.34 \text{ ft}^2 = 32.69 \text{ ft}^2$
S.A. $= 32.69 \text{ ft}^2 +$ area of two bases $=$
$32.69 \text{ ft}^2 + (2.5 \text{ ft} \times 1 \text{ ft} \times 2) = 32.69 \text{ ft}^2 + 5 \text{ ft}^2 = 37.69 \text{ ft}^2$

4) Area of front and back $= 1.75 \text{ m} \times 4.52 \text{ m} \times 2 = 15.82 \text{ m}^2$
Area of sides $= 0.86 \text{ m} \times 4.52 \text{ m} \times 2 = 7.77 \text{ m}^2$
L.A. $= 15.82 \text{ m}^2 + 7.77 \text{ m}^2 = 23.59 \text{ m}^2$
S.A. $= 23.59 \text{ m}^2 +$ area of two bases $=$
$23.59 \text{ m}^2 + (1.75 \text{ m} \times 0.86 \text{ m} \times 2) = 23.59 \text{ m}^2 + 3.01 \text{ m}^2 = 26.6 \text{ ft}^2$

Page 174, **Practice**

1) $A = LW = 6 \text{ ft} \times 15 \text{ ft} = 90 \text{ ft}^2$
$90 \text{ ft}^2 \times \$5.25 = \$472.50$

2) Area of rectangle = $3.5 \text{ ft} \times 4.75 \text{ ft} = 16.63 \text{ ft}^2$
Area of circle = $\pi r^2 = \pi \times (1.75 \text{ ft})^2 = 9.62$
Half a circle = $9.62 \text{ ft}^2 \div 2 = 4.81 \text{ ft}^2$
Total area = $16.63 \text{ ft}^2 + 4.81 \text{ ft}^2 = 21.44 \text{ ft}^2$

3) Area = $\pi r^2 = \pi \times (6 \text{ m})^2 = 113.1 \text{ m}^2$

4) a. area of doors = $3 \text{ ft} \times 7 \text{ ft} \times 2 = 42 \text{ ft}^2$
area of window = $2.5 \text{ ft} \times 4 \text{ ft} = 10 \text{ ft}^2$
area of front and back wall = $8 \text{ ft} \times 9 \text{ ft} \times 2 = 144 \text{ ft}^2$
area of side walls = $10 \text{ ft} \times 9 \text{ ft} \times 2 = 180 \text{ ft}^2$
Total area of room = $180 \text{ ft}^2 + 144 \text{ ft}^2 - (42 \text{ ft}^2 + 10 \text{ ft}^2) = 272 \text{ ft}^2$

b. area of sheet of drywall = $4 \text{ ft} \times 8 \text{ ft} = 32 \text{ ft}^2$
number of sheets of drywall = $272 \text{ ft}^2 \div 32 \text{ ft}^2 = 8.5$
Round up 8.5 to 9
$9 \times \$38.98 = \$350.82$

5) Area of top and bottom of cupboard = $3 \text{ ft} \times 2.5 \text{ ft} \times 2 = 15 \text{ ft}^2$
Area of back and front = $3 \text{ ft} \times 4.75 \text{ ft} \times 2 = 28.5 \text{ ft}^2$
Area of sides = $2.5 \text{ ft} \times 4.75 \text{ ft} \times 2 = 23.75 \text{ ft}^2$
Total area = $(15 \text{ ft}^2 + 28.5 \text{ ft}^2 + 23.75 \text{ ft}^2) \times 5 = 336.25 \text{ ft}^2$

6) Front and back of closet = $6.5 \text{ ft} \times 8 \text{ ft} \times 2 = 104 \text{ ft}^2$
Sides of closet = $4.5 \text{ ft} \times 8 \text{ ft} \times 2 = 72 \text{ ft}^2$
number of square feet of pine = $104 \text{ ft}^2 + 72 \text{ ft}^2 - 21 \text{ ft}^2 = 155 \text{ ft}^2$

7) Area of roof = $16 \text{ ft} \times 45.75 \text{ ft} \times 2 = 1\ 464 \text{ ft}^2$

8) Area of one piece of panelling = $4 \text{ ft} \times 8 \text{ ft} = 32 \text{ ft}^2$
Cost of one piece of panelling = $32 \text{ ft}^2 \times \$1.25 = \$40.00$
36 pieces of panelling = $\$40.00 \times 36 = \$1\ 440.00$

ANSWER KEY

GEOMETRY - VOLUME

Page 180, **Calculating Volume**

1) $V = LWH = 4 \text{ m} \times 3 \text{ m} \times 6 \text{ m} = 72 \text{ m}^3$

2) $V = LWH = 2.5 \text{ m} \times 1 \text{ m} \times 0.6 \text{ m} = 1.5 \text{ m}^3$

3) $V = \pi r^2 h = \pi \times (2 \text{ ft})^2 \times 12 \text{ ft} = 150.8 \text{ ft}^3$

4) $35 \text{ cm} = 0.35 \text{ m}$
$V = \pi r^2 h = \pi \times (0.35 \text{ m})^2 \times 1.4 \text{ m} = 0.54 \text{ m}^3$

5) radius = diameter ÷ 2 = 4.2 ÷ 2 = 2.1 ft
7 ft — 9 in = 7.75 ft
$V = \pi r^2 h = \pi \times (2.1 \text{ ft})^2 \times 7.75 \text{ ft} = 107.37 \text{ ft}^3$

6) radius = diameter ÷ 2 = 0.45 ÷ 2 = 0.23 m
$V = \pi r^2 h = \pi \times (0.23 \text{ m})^2 \times 3.4 \text{ m} = 0.57 \text{ m}^3$

7) $V = \dfrac{\pi r^2 h}{3} = \dfrac{\pi \times (2 \text{ ft})^2 \times 6 \text{ ft}}{3} = \dfrac{75.4 \text{ ft}^3}{3} = 25.13 \text{ ft}^3$

8) $V = \dfrac{\pi r^2 h}{3} = \dfrac{\pi \times (1.2 \text{ m})^2 \times 5 \text{ m}}{3} = \dfrac{22.62 \text{ m}^3}{3} = 7.54 \text{ m}^3$

9) $25 \text{ cm} = 0.25 \text{ m}$
$V = \dfrac{\pi r^2 h}{3} = \dfrac{\pi \times (0.25 \text{ m})^2 \times 1.5 \text{ m}}{3} = \dfrac{0.29 \text{ m}^3}{3} = 0.1 \text{ m}^3$

10) diameter = r × 2 = 2 × 2 = 4 ft
$V = \dfrac{\pi d^3}{6} = \dfrac{\pi \times (4 \text{ ft})^3}{6} = \dfrac{201.06 \text{ ft}^3}{6} = 33.51 \text{ ft}^3$

11) diameter = r × 2 = 75 × 2 = 150 cm
$V = \dfrac{\pi d^3}{6} = \dfrac{\pi \times (150 \text{ cm})^3}{6} = \dfrac{10\,602\,875.21 \text{ cm}^3}{6} = 1\,767\,145.87 \text{ cm}^3$

12) $V = 2.59 \times s^2 \times h = 2.59 \times (6 \text{ in})^2 \times 36 \text{ in} = 3\,356.64 \text{ in}^3$

13) $V = 2.59 \times s^2 \times h = 2.59 \times (32 \text{ mm})^2 \times 995 \text{ mm} = 2\,638\,899.2 \text{ mm}^3$

14) 10" = 83'
$V = LWH = 3.5 \text{ ft} \times 1.5 \text{ ft} \times 0.83 \text{ ft} = 4.36 \text{ ft}^3$

15) $V = s^3 = (47 \text{ cm})^3 = 103\,823 \text{ cm}^3$

16) radius = diameter ÷ 2 = 60 cm ÷ 2 = 30 cm
30 cm = 0.30 m
$V = \pi r^2 h = \pi \times (0.30 \text{ m})^2 \times 3.5 \text{ m} = 0.99 \text{ m}^3$

17) $V = \dfrac{\pi d^3}{6} = \dfrac{\pi \times (3.2 \text{ ft})^3}{6} = \dfrac{102.94 \text{ ft}^3}{6} = 17.16 \text{ ft}^3$

18) 125 cm = 1.25 m
radius = diameter ÷ 2 = 1.25 ÷ 2 =

$V = \dfrac{\pi r^2 h}{3} = \dfrac{\pi \times (0.625 \text{ m})^2 \times 2.5 \text{ m}}{3} = \dfrac{3.07 \text{ m}}{3} = 1.02 \text{ m}^3$

19) 29 in = 2.42 ft
$V = 2.59 \times s^2 \times h = 2.59 \times (2.54 \text{ ft})^2 \times 2.42 = 40.44 \text{ ft}^3$

20) $V = s^3 = (18 \text{ in})^3 = 5\,832 \text{ in}^3$

Page 186, Calculating the Volume of Complex Shapes

1) 6 in = 0.5 ft
5 in = 0.42 ft
9 in = 0.75 ft
Volume of wall = LWH = 15 ft × 0.5 ft × 6 ft = 45 ft³
Volume of footing = LWH = 15 ft × 0.75 ft × 0.42 ft = 4.73 ft³
Total volume = 45 ft³ + 4.73 ft³ = 49.73 ft³

2) Volume of large rectangular solid = LWH = 20 ft × 5 ft × 9 ft = 900 ft³

Volume of small rectangular solid = LWH = 5 ft × 5 ft × 4 ft = 100 ft³
Total volume = 900 ft³ + 100 ft³ = 1 000 ft³

3) Volume of cube = s³ = (4 m)³ = 64 m³
Volume of rectangular solid = 4 m × 4 m × 8 m = 128 m³
Total volume = 64 m³ + 128 m³ = 192 m³

4) Volume = LWH = 400 mm × 100 mm × 40 mm = 1 600 000 mm³
Total volume = 1 600 000 mm³ ÷ 2 = 800 000 mm³

5) Volume of large rectangular solid =
LWH = 6.4 m × 2.3 m × 2 m = 29.44 m³

Volume of small rectangular solid =
LWH = 6.4 m × 1.2 m × 0.9 m = 6.91 m³

Total volume = 29.44 m³ – 6.91 m³ = 22.53 m³

6) radius = diameter ÷ 2 = 18 cm ÷ 2 = 9 cm
$V = \pi r^2 h = \pi \times (9 \text{ cm})^2 \times 42 \text{ cm} = 10\ 687.7 \text{ cm}^3$
Total volume = 10 687.7 cm³ ÷ 2 = 5 343.85 cm³

7) Volume of cylinder = $\pi r^2 h = \pi \times (3 \text{ ft})^2 \times 7 \text{ ft} = 197.92 \text{ ft}^3$
Volume of rectangular solid = LWH = 9 ft × 9 ft × 4 ft = 324 ft³
Total volume = 197.92 ft³ + 324 ft³ = 521.92 ft³

8) Volume of rectangular solid = LWH = 21 ft × 8 ft × 10 ft = 1 680 ft³
radius = diameter ÷ 2 = 8 ÷ 2 = 4 ft
Volume of cylinder = $\pi r^2 h = \pi \times (4 \text{ ft})^2 \times 21 \text{ ft} = 1\ 055.58 \text{ ft}^3$
Volume of half cylinder = 1 055.58 ft³ ÷ 2 = 527.79 ft³
Total volume = 1 680 ft³ + 527.79 ft³ = 2 207.79 ft³

9) radius = diameter ÷ 2 = 9 ÷ 2 = 4.5 in
Volume of large cylinder = $\pi r^2 h = \pi \times (4.5 \text{ in})^2 \times 12.75 \text{ in} = 811.12 \text{ in}^3$
radius = diameter ÷ 2 = 3.25 ÷ 2 = 1.63 in
Volume of small cylinder = $\pi r^2 h = \pi \times (1.63 \text{ in})^2 \times 12.75 \text{ in} = 106.42 \text{ in}^3$
Total volume = 811.12 in³ − 106.42 in³ = 704.7 in³

10) Volume of large rectangular solid = LWH = 7 ft × 3 ft × 6 ft = 126 ft³
Volume of small rectangular solid = LWH =
1.5 ft × 3 ft × 2.1 ft = 9.45 ft³
Total volume = 126 ft³ − 9.45 ft³ = 116.55 ft³

11) Volume of large rectangular solid = LWH =
6.35 m × 2.3 m × 4.2 m = 61.34 m³
Volume of small rectangular solid = LWH =
0.7 m × 2.3 m × 1.25 m = 2.01 m³
Total volume =
61.34 m³ − (2.01 m³ × 3) = 61.34 m³ − 6.03 m³ = 55.31 m³

12) Volume of rectangular solid = LWH = 7 m × 2.5 m × 3 m = 52.5 m³
radius = diameter ÷ 2 = 2.5 ÷ 2 = 1.25 m
Volume of cylinder = $\pi r^2 h = \pi \times (1.25 \text{ m})^2 \times 7 \text{ m} = 34.36 \text{ m}^3$
Volume of half cylinder = 34.36 m³ ÷ 2 = 17.18 m³
Total volume = 52.5 m³ + 17.18 m³ = 69.68 m³

13) radius = diameter ÷ 2 = 9 ÷ 2 = 4.5 ft
Volume of cylinder = $\pi r^2 h = \pi \times (4.5 \text{ ft})^2 \times 15 \text{ ft} = 954.26 \text{ ft}^3$
Volume of cone =
$$\frac{\pi r^2 h}{3} = \frac{\pi \times (4.5 \text{ ft})^2 \times 1.5 \text{ ft}}{3} = \frac{95.43 \text{ ft}^3}{3} = 31.81 \text{ ft}^3$$
Total volume = 954.26 ft³ + 31.81 ft³ = 986.07 ft³

14) radius = diameter ÷ 2 = 1.25 ÷ 2 = 0.63 m

Volume of cylinder = $\pi r^2 h = \pi \times (0.63 \text{ m})^2 \times 10 \text{ m} = 12.47 \text{ m}^3$

Volume of sphere = $\dfrac{\pi d^3}{6} = \dfrac{\pi \times (1.25 \text{ m})^3}{6} = \dfrac{6.14 \text{ m}^3}{6} = 1.02 \text{ m}^3$

Total volume = 12.47 m³ + 1.02 m³ = 13.49 m³

15) radius = diameter ÷ 2 = 10.5 ÷ 2 = 5.25 ft

Volume of cylinder = $\pi r^2 h = \pi \times (5.25 \text{ ft})^2 \times 27 \text{ ft} = 2337.93 \text{ ft}^3$

Volume of sphere = $\dfrac{\pi d^3}{6} = \dfrac{\pi \times (10.5 \text{ ft})^3}{6} = \dfrac{3\,636.79 \text{ ft}^3}{6} = 606.13 \text{ ft}^3$

Volume of half a sphere = 606.13 ft³ ÷ 2 = 303.07 ft³

Total volume = 2 337.93 ft³ + 303.07 ft³ = 2 641 ft³

Page 192, Calculating the height or diameter when you know the volume

1) $V = LWH$

36 yd³ = 3 yd × 1.5 yd × h

36 yd³ = 4.5 yd² × h

$\dfrac{36 \text{ yd}^3}{4.5 \text{ yd}^2} = h$

8 yd = h

2) $V = LWH$

18 m³ = 3.6 m × W × 2.1 m

18 m³ = 7.56 m² × W

$\dfrac{18 \text{ m}^3}{7.56 \text{ m}^2} = W$

2.38 m = h

3) $V = \pi r^2 h$

67 ft³ = π × r² × 6.5 ft

67 ft³ = 20.42 ft × r²

$\dfrac{67 \text{ ft}^3}{20.42 \text{ ft}} = r^2$

3.28 ft² = r²

$\sqrt{3.28}$ ft = r

1.81 ft = r

4) $V = \pi r^2 h$

$188\ \text{in}^3 = \pi \times (22\ \text{in})^2 \times h$

$188\ \text{in}^3 = 1\ 520.53\ \text{in}^2 \times h$

$\dfrac{188\ \text{in}^3}{1\ 520.53\ \text{in}^2} = h$

$0.12\ \text{in} = h$

5) $V = \pi r^2 h$

$450\ \text{cm}^3 = \pi \times r^2 \times 224\ \text{cm}$

$450\ \text{cm}^3 = 703.72\ \text{cm} \times r^2$

$\dfrac{450\ \text{cm}^3}{703.72\ \text{cm}} = r^2$

$0.64\ \text{cm} = r^2$

$\sqrt{0.64\ \text{cm}} = r$

$0.8\ \text{cm} = r$

$d = 0.8\ \text{cm} \times 2 = 1.6\ \text{cm}$

6) $V = \dfrac{\pi r^2 h}{3}$

$234\ \text{ft}^3 = \dfrac{\pi \times (10\ \text{ft})^2 \times h}{3}$

$234\ \text{ft}^3 = \dfrac{314.16\ \text{ft}^2 \times h}{3}$

$234\ \text{ft}^3 \times 3 = 314.16\ \text{ft}^2 \times h$

$\dfrac{702\ \text{ft}^3}{314.16\ \text{ft}^3} = h$

$2.23\ \text{ft} = h$

7) $V = \dfrac{\pi r^2 h}{3}$

$234\ \text{ft}^3 = \dfrac{\pi \times r^2 \times 15.5\ \text{ft}}{3}$

$234\ \text{ft}^3 = \dfrac{48.7\ \text{ft} \times r^2}{3}$

$234\ \text{ft}^3 \times 3 = 48.7\ \text{ft} \times r^2$

$\dfrac{702\ \text{ft}^3}{48.7\ \text{ft}} = r^2$

$14.41\ \text{ft} = r^2$

$\sqrt{14.41\ \text{ft}} = r$

$3.8\ \text{ft} = r$

diameter = radius × 2 = 3.8 × 2 = 7.6 ft

Page 194, **Practice**

1) 1 ft = 0.33 yd
   V = LWH = 6 yd × 3 yd × 0.33 yd = 5.94 yd³ = 6 yd³

2) 400 mm = 0.4 m
   V = LWH = 3 m × 0.4 m × 12 m = 14.4 m³ = 15 m³

3) V = LWH = 13 m × 6 m × 0.3 m = 23.4 m³ = 24 m³

4) V = LWH = 5.5 ft × 2 ft × 3.6 ft = 39.6 ft³
   27 ft³ = 1 yd³
   39.6 ft³ ÷ 27 ft³ = 1.47 yd³
   1.47 yd³ × 0.3 = 0.44 yd³
   Total volume of fill required = 1.47 yd³ + 0.44 yd³ = 1.91 yd³ = 2 yd³

5) radius = diameter ÷ 2 = 6.5 m ÷ 2 = = 3.25 m

   $$V = \frac{\pi r^2 h}{3}$$

   $$V = \frac{\pi \times (3.25 \text{ m})^2 \times 2.3 \text{ m}}{3}$$

   $$V = \frac{76.32 \text{ m}^3}{3}$$

   V = 25.44 m³ = 26 m³

6) V = LWH = 39 ft × 1.6 ft × 5 ft = 312 ft³
   312 ft³ ÷ 27 ft³ = 11.56 yd³ = 12 yd³

7) V = πr²h
   V = π × (0.4 m)² × 4.5 m
   V = 2.26 m³
   Total volume = 2.26 m³ × 8 = 18.08 m³ = 19 m³

8) 24 in = 2 ft
   V = LWH = 2 ft × 2 ft × 2 ft = 8 ft³
   Total volume = 8 ft³ × 9 = 72 ft³
   72 ft³ ÷ 27 ft³ = 2.67 yd³ = 3 m³

9)

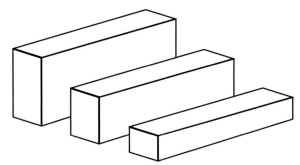

$7\frac{1}{2}" = 0.625'$
V = LWH = 4.5 ft × 1 ft × 1.88 ft = 8.46 ft³
V = LWH = 4.5 ft × 1 ft × 1.255 ft = 5.65 ft³
V = LWH = 4.5 ft × 1 ft × 0.63 ft = 2.84 ft³
Total volume = 8.46 ft³ + 5.65 ft³ + 2.84 ft³ = 16.95 ft³
16.95 ft³ ÷ 27 = 0.63 yd³ = 1 yd³

10)   V = LWH = 9 ft × 15 ft × 6.4 ft = 864 ft³
Allowance for compaction = 864 ft³ × 0.25 = 216 ft³
Total fill needed = 864 ft³ + 216 ft³ = 1 080 ft³

$$V = \frac{\pi r^2 h}{3} = \frac{\pi \times (6 \text{ ft})^2 \times 7 \text{ ft}}{3} = \frac{791.68}{3} = 263.89 \text{ ft}^3$$

Allowance for compaction = 263.89 ft³ × 0.25 = 65.97 ft³
Total fill available = 263.89 ft³ – 65.97 ft³ = 197.92 ft³
The contractor needs to order more fill =
1 080 ft³ – 197.92 ft³ = 882.08 ft³
882.08 ft³ ÷ 27 = 32.67 yd³ = 33 yd³

11)   The side of the pool is a trapezoid. Use the side as the base.

$$\text{area of base} = \left(\frac{b_1 + b_2}{2}\right)h = \left(\frac{3 + 12}{2}\right)80 = 7.5 \times 80 = 600 \text{ ft}^2$$

volume of pool = area of base × h = 600 ft² × 25 ft = 15 000 ft³
15 000 ft³ ÷ 27 ft³ = 555.56 yd³
555.56 yd³ ÷ 27 yd³ = 20.6 = 21
There are 21 truckloads.

12)   Volume of big rectangular solid = LWH =
145 ft × 75 ft × 8.5 ft = 92 437.5 ft³

Volume of small rectangular solid = LWH =
65 ft × 40 ft × 8.5 ft = 22 100 ft³

Total volume = 92 437.5 ft³ – 22 100 ft³ = 70 337.5 ft³
70 337.5 ft³ ÷ 27 ft³ = 2 605.1 yd³
2 605.1 yd³ ÷ 27 yd³ = 96.49 = 97 truckloads

ANSWER KEY

GEOMETRY - RIGHT-ANGLE TRIANGLES

Page 202, **Angles**

1) a)   ∠Y, ∠XYZ   b)   ∠2, ∠Y

   c)   ∠XZY, ∠Z   d)   ∠YXZ, ∠X

2) a)   180°   b)   180°

   c)   180°   d)   360°

3) a) 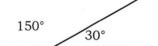   b)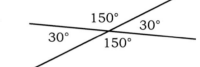

   c)   d)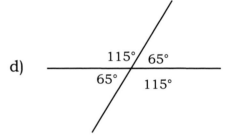

4) a)   30°   b)   180°

   c)   180°   d)   100°

   e)   150°   f)   300°

Page 204, **Calculating the Missing Angle in a Triangle**

1)   45°   2)   60°   3)   60°

4)   20°   5)   25°   6)   20°

7)   75°   8)   33°   9)   10°

10)   64°

Page 206, **Calculating Degrees, Minutes and Seconds**

1) a)   1' 1"   b)   1' 59"   c)   1' 12"   d)   1' 52"

2) a)   3'   b)   3' 3"   c)   1' 17"   d)   4' 2"

Page 207, **Calculating Degrees, Minutes and Seconds**

1) a) 1° 1'   b) 1° 59'   c) 47'   d) 1° 20'

2) a) 1° 50'   b) 1° 35'   c) 4° 15'   d) 1°

Page 208, **Adding Angles**

1) 42° 51' 48"   2) 9° 2' 50"   3) 76° 33' 19"   4) 105° 52' 11"

5) 90°   6) 48° 13' 11"   7) 76° 59' 57"   8) 93° 1' 33"

9) 72° 19' 0"   10) 34° 42' 2"   11) 144°17' 33" 12) 180°

13) 248° 40'   14) 80° 1' 12"   15) 180°   16) 40° 8' 1"

Page 209, **Subtracting Angles**

1) 18° 12' 26"   2) 22° 59' 29"   3) 1° 1' 11"   4) 33° 13' 34"

5) 12° 15' 28"   6) 14° 42' 5"   7) 0° 1' 6"   8) 72° 55' 52"

9) 10° 51' 59"   10) 68° 17' 21" 11) 0° 22' 1"   12) 18° 12' 28"

13) 11° 57' 2"   14) 22° 59' 59" 15) 8° 48' 51"   16) 63° 2' 0"

Page 212, **Pythagorean Theorem**

1) $1.8^2 + 2.7^2 = travel^2$

        $\sqrt{10.53} = travel$

        $3.24 \text{ m} = travel$

2) $7^2 + 11^2 = travel^2$

        $\sqrt{170} = travel$

        $13.04 \text{ ft} = travel$

3) $15.3^2 - 2.5^2 = run$

        $\sqrt{227.84} = run$

        $15.09 \text{ m} = run$

4) $20^2 - 16^2 = rise$

        $\sqrt{144} = rise$

        $12 \text{ ft} = rise$

5) $62\,267^2 - 2\,900^2 = rise^2$

        $\sqrt{3\,868\,769\,289} = rise^2$

        $62\,199.43 \text{ mm} = rise$

6) $1\,000^2 + 2\,455^2 = travel^2$

        $\sqrt{7\,027\,025} = travel$

        $2\,650.85 \text{ mm} = travel$

7) $4\,236^2 + 1\,955^2 = travel^2$

        $\sqrt{21\,765\,721} = travel$

        $4\,665.37 \text{ mm} = travel$

        $4\,665.37 + 850 = 5\,515.37 \text{ mm}$

8) $1\,829^2 + 1\,355^2 = travel^2$

        $\sqrt{5\,181\,266} = travel$

        $2\,276.24 \text{ mm} = travel$

        $2\,276.24 + 305 = 2\,581.24 \text{ mm}$

9) $2\,400^2 + 1\,500^2 = travel^2$

        $\sqrt{8\,010\,000} = travel^2$

        $2\,830.19 \text{ mm} = travel$

        $2\,830.19 + 350 = 3\,180.19 \text{ mm}$

10)   6 875² + 3 658² = travel²

$\sqrt{60\ 646\ 589}$ = travel²

7 787.59 = travel

7 787.59 + 875 = 8 662.59 mm

Page 214, **Trigonometry**

1)
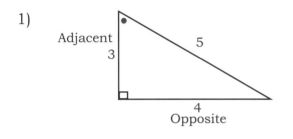

2)
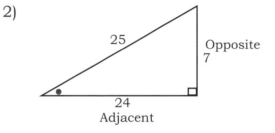

3)
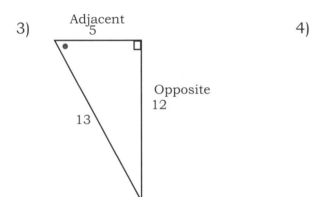

4)
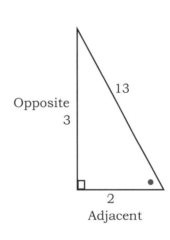

5)
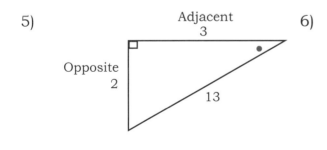

6)
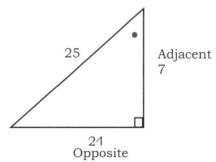

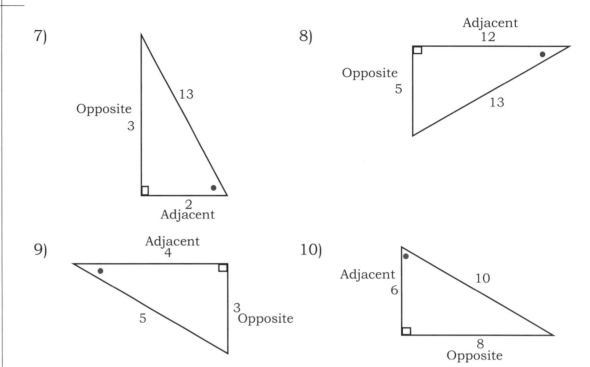

7)

Opposite 3
13
2 Adjacent

8)

Adjacent 12
Opposite 5
13

9)

Adjacent 4
5
3 Opposite

10)

Adjacent 6
10
8 Opposite

Page 218, Calculating the Length of a Side

1) hypotenuse = $\dfrac{\text{opposite}}{\sin}$ = $\dfrac{3.1}{\sin 46°}$ = 4.31 ft

2) hypotenuse = $\dfrac{\text{adjacent}}{\cos}$ = $\dfrac{16}{\cos 50°}$ = 24.89 cm

3) adjacent = cos × hypotenuse = cos 33° × 4.25 = 3.56 ft

4) opposite = tan × adjacent = tan 63° × 1.35 = 2.65 m

5) adjacent = cos × hypotenuse = cos 27° × 6.25 = 5.57 ft

6) hypotenuse = $\dfrac{\text{adjacent}}{\cos}$ = $\dfrac{96}{\cos 71°}$ = 294.87 in

7) opposite = tan × adjacent = tan 47° × 15 = 16.09 in

8) opposite = sin × hypotenuse = sin 37° × 4.3 = 2.59 m

9) hypotenuse = $\dfrac{\text{adjacent}}{\cos}$ = $\dfrac{546}{\cos 42°}$ = 734.72 cm

10) adjacent = $\dfrac{\text{opposite}}{\tan}$ = $\dfrac{3.6}{\tan 65°}$ = 1.68 ft

Page 222, **Calculating the Size of an Angle**

1) $\sin = \dfrac{\text{opposite}}{\text{hypotenuse}} = \dfrac{2.3}{6.4} = 0.0359375$

   Press 2nd function. Press sin. 21.06°

2) $\cos = \dfrac{\text{adjacent}}{\text{hypotenuse}} = \dfrac{150}{252} = 0.595238095$

   Press 2nd function. Press cos. 53.47°

3) $\cos = \dfrac{\text{adjacent}}{\text{hypotenuse}} = \dfrac{49}{69} = 0.710144928$

   Press 2nd function. Press cos. 44.75°

4) $\sin = \dfrac{\text{opposite}}{\text{hypotenuse}} = \dfrac{3.33}{5.25} = 0.634285714$

   Press 2nd function. Press sin. 39.37°

5) $\tan = \dfrac{\text{opposite}}{\text{adjacent}} = \dfrac{0.155}{1.24} = 0.125$

   Press 2nd function. Press tan. 7.13°

6) $\sin = \dfrac{\text{opposite}}{\text{hypotenuse}} = \dfrac{1.5}{4.17} = 0.35971223$

   Press 2nd function. Press sin. 21.08°

7) $\cos = \dfrac{\text{adjacent}}{\text{hypotenuse}} = \dfrac{2.5}{3.1} = 0.806451613$

   Press 2nd function. Press cos. 36.25°

8) $\sin = \dfrac{\text{opposite}}{\text{hypotenuse}} = \dfrac{15}{26.5} = 0.566037736$

   Press 2nd function. Press sin. 34.47°

9) $\tan = \dfrac{\text{opposite}}{\text{adjacent}} = \dfrac{2.42}{3.42} = 0.707602339$

   Press 2nd function. Press tan. 35.28°

10) $\sin = \dfrac{\text{opposite}}{\text{hypotenuse}} = \dfrac{1.78}{5.46} = 0.326007326$

   Press 2nd function. Press sin. 19.03°

Page 226, **Working with Multi-sided Shapes**

1) angle A = 360 ÷ 12 = 30°
    angle B = 90 − 30 = 60°

    side a = tan × adjacent = tan 30° × 20 = 11.55 ft

    side c = $\dfrac{\text{adjacent}}{\cos}$ = $\dfrac{20}{\cos 30°}$ = 23.1 ft

2) angle A = 360 ÷ 14 = 25.71°
    angle B = 90 − 25.71 = 64.29°

    side a = sin × hypotenuse = sin 25.71° × 24 = 10.41 ft

    side b = cos × hypotenuse = cos 25.71° × 24 = 21.62 ft

3) angle A = 360 ÷ 16 = 22.5°
    angle B = 90 − 22.5 = 67.5°

    side b = $\dfrac{\text{opposite}}{\tan}$ = $\dfrac{8}{\tan 22.5°}$ = 19.31 m

    side c = $\dfrac{\text{opposite}}{\sin}$ = $\dfrac{8}{\sin 22.5°}$ = 20.91 m

Page 226, **Practice**

1) $a^2 + b^2 = c^2$

    $5^2 + 12^2 = c^2$

    $169 = c^2$

    $\sqrt{169} = c$

    $13 = c$

    The diagonal should measure 13 ft.

2) $a^2 + b^2 = c^2$

    $8^2 + 15^2 = c^2$

    $289 = c^2$

    $\sqrt{289} = c$

    $17 = c$

    The length of the brace is 17 feet.

3) $c^2 - a^2 = b^2$

    $6.5^2 - 6^2 = b^2$

    $6.25 = b^2$

    $\sqrt{6.25} = b$

    $2.5 = b$

    The brace must be secured 2.5 m from the wall.

4) $a^2 + b^2 = c^2$
    $9.2^2 + 5.6^2 = c^2$
    $116 = c^2$
    $\sqrt{116} = c$
    $10.77 = c$
    The diagonal length of the staircase is 10.77 ft.

5) $a^2 + b^2 = c^2$
    $8^2 + 9.2^2 = c^2$
    $148.64 = c^2$
    $\sqrt{148.64} = c$
    $12.19 = c$
    $12.19 + 3 = 15.19$
    The length of the rafter needs to be 15.19 ft.

6) $c^2 - a^2 = b^2$
    $71.1^2 - 46.6^2 = b^2$
    $2\,883.65 = b^2$
    $\sqrt{2\,883.65} = b$
    $53.70 = b$
    The length of the lot is 53.70 ft.

7) $\text{hypotenuse} = \dfrac{\text{opposite}}{\sin} = \dfrac{15}{\sin 75°} = 15.5 \text{ ft}$

    $15.5 + 3 = 18.5$ feet
    The ladder needs to be at least 18.53 feet long.

8) $\text{hypotenuse} = \dfrac{\text{opposite}}{\sin} = \dfrac{6.33}{\sin 40°} = 9.85 \text{ ft}$

    The length of the rafter is 9.85 ft.

9) $x = \dfrac{\text{adjacent}}{\cos} = \dfrac{9.3}{\cos 25°} = 10.26 \text{ ft}$

10) angle A = $360° \div 16 = 22.5°$
    opposite = tan × adjacent = $\tan 22.5° \times 3 = 1.24$ ft
    $1.24 \times 2 = 2.48$ ft
    The distance between holes centre-to-centre is 2.30 feet.